MEDIA REVIEWS

"Compelling in its sincerity and thought-provoking in its content, Inca Fire! Offers a new and well-defined path to wisdom and spiritual power."
- NAPRA ReView

"A compelling spiritual adventure story set in Machu Picchu, Peru. Along with author Val Jon Farris, experience the seven dimensions of knowing that will transform you and forever change the way you look at your life."
- The New Times

"Farris brings a fresh and intelligent dialogue to widely accepted New Age principles. Highly recommended for any library looking to invigorate its spiritual collection."
- Today's Librarian

"Farris' masterful storytelling abilities draw the reader into a fascinating world of human inspiration, physical challenge and divine intervention. A fascinating read!"
- The Leading Edge Review

"To anyone who considers themselves to be seekers of a lost humane awareness, I say read Inca Fire! Perhaps heat and light will generate warmth, compassion and a new world vision."
- The Midwest Book Review

INCA FIRE! LIGHT OF THE MASTERS

Published By

Auburn, California

Manufactured in the United States of America

Farris, Val Jon.
    Inca fire! : light of the masters / Val Jon
Farris. -- 1 st ed.
    p. cm.
    Includes bibliographical references and index.
    ISBN: 1-928621-02-3

    1. Spiritual life--New Age movement.
2. Spiritual biography. 3. Visions. 4. Machu Picchu
Site (Peru)--Miscellanea. I. Title.

BP605.N48F37 1999   299'.42
              QBI99-1100

To Rouge

You are beautiful in *every* way.
May the winds of eternity always carry you home.

ACKNOWLEDGMENTS

I would like to thank the following people for their support with this book. In addition to providing superlative counsel and advice, each of them participated with passion and heartfelt dedication.

* Cynthia Stevens, for her undying vision, heart and editing endurance, which provided crucial insight into the manuscript's readability and "feel."
* John Walker, for his literary accountability, witty sense of humor and invaluable insights about reader comprehension and acceptance.
* Kathy & Gradie Johnson, for their eternal friendship and pivotal feedback regarding chapter sequencing and story line integrity.
* Aimee Barajas for her contributions to proper grammar, sentence structure and important editorial comments.
* Matt Barajas for his graphic design contributions.
* Cynthia Frank and John Fremont from Cypress House Publishing Company for their "launch guidance."
* Doug Perry for his inventive and creative web site designs and internet marketing strategies.
* A very special thanks to Marty Petersen for the awesome book cover, poster design and map creation.

Val Jon pointing to the mysterious summit of Wayna Picchu which stands high above the ruins of Machu Picchu.

One of many ancient Inca temples with its open doorway leading to the heavens.

TABLE OF CONTENTS

Land of peace above the sky
Mysterious stones and ancient shrines
Enchanted souls and timeless eyes
On the condor's wings to the end of time

The Temple of the Stars located in the city of Cusco was used by the Incas to chart the heavens and measure celestial movements.

INTRODUCTION

STEPPING INTO THE "BURN ZONE"

In the summer of 1998, I embarked on an expedition that led me to a mysterious pinnacle of granite on the northern slope of the ancient Inca ruins of Machu Picchu. On the night of July 9, under a full moon, I received a flurry of inspired messages, seven to be exact, that triggered a sequence of events which redefined the meaning and purpose of my life. The seventeen chapters in this book go into great detail about each of the messages, the events that transformed my life and the means by which you, the reader, can reap the benefits of my journey through participating in a literary adventure.

Visiting a place like Machu Picchu, Peru, is not new for me. I have been a seeker and an explorer for as long as I can remember. My inquisitive nature began when I was a child. Like all kids, I had a million questions about life. Why is a tree called a tree? Why do dogs bark? Where is heaven? Where do babies come from? And Mom, why won't you answer any more of my questions? As a teenager, in addition to being driven by hormones, I was inspired by reading about the great thinkers of the world. I recall reading a passage from Dante's *Inferno* in which man is warned about the downside of desire. He's shown the eternal damnation that awaits him if he indulges. And after the warning, what does he do? You guessed it. He plunges headfirst into hell.

Human nature is a strange and wonderful thing. I enjoy learning about it and sharing its complexities with others. As a Behavioral

Scientist (which, by the way, is nothing more than a glorified people watcher), I have spent the better part of two decades teaching in the private and public sectors. By day, I design and implement leadership programs for national and international corporations and by night I conduct self-awareness seminars and poetry events. (I have included some of my poetry and prose as chapter introductions in this book). As a Gemini, my dual career couldn't be better suited to me. I get to travel to both ends of the spectrum: the world of cognition and results, and the world of creativity and spirit.

In my spare time, when I'm not on the road, I enjoy riding my scooter, a 1450 cc Harley-Davidson, mountaineering, scuba diving, listening to music and spending time with my partner, Cynthia Stevens. I'm extremely passionate about life and enjoy experiences that challenge me personally and spiritually. My Italian, Irish and Cherokee Indian heritage may have something to do with my outgoing nature.

After conducting a two-week management training program for a company in Sao Paulo, Brazil, last summer, I decided to take some time off and explore the Peruvian Andes, particularly the ruins at Machu Picchu. Something about the Inca ruins captivated me. For many years I had experienced a strange kind of "pull" to go there. Whenever I get that kind of feeling about my life, I know I had better respond, because it usually means there's something of great importance for me to learn or experience. The pull I experienced to visit Machu Picchu, however, was very different from others I've felt. Not only had I felt the pull many times over the years, it got progressively more intense, until I couldn't put off responding to it any longer. Little did I know that finally answering the call would cast me into a spellbinding "burn zone" of personal insight, drama and revelation. The burn zone of the *Inca Fire* is like a raging flame that hungrily consumes logic and reason, transforming it into a compelling blaze of insight and wisdom—a wisdom that powerfully illuminates both the capabilities of the human mind and the indestructible nature of the soul. By "soul" I mean the paradoxical part of us that is both human and divine. It is that inner sanctum, that private place within our hearts that provides a bridge between our mortal existence and the infinite embrace of the divine.

I call the wisdom contained within the *Inca Fire's* burn zone the *Light of the Masters*. Its multifaceted "light" manifests as seven dimensions of knowing: *Humility, Eternality, Truth, Passion, Sovereignty, Faith and Service*. Although these terms may be familiar, it is their cumulative power I will focus on in this book. Why these seven and not a hundred others? I'm sure there are many valid dimensions, but these were revealed to me during my quest, so they are the ones I have written about. A "dimension" is an orientation, perspective, or position to view from.

Dimensions of knowing are the *ways* we know something rather than *what* we know. The more ways we have of knowing, the more flexible and capable we can be with our knowledge. It may be that true wisdom, rather than being an accumulation of intellect or knowledge, is the result of possessing multiple ways of knowing how to access and utilize our knowledge base. This is evident in the fact that there are plenty of very "intelligent" people who don't seem to be very "wise."

The first step to gaining multiple dimensions or ways of knowing lies in shifting out of our familiar "default" perspective about ourselves into a broader, more expansive view. Our default perspective is made up of our identity, attitudes, behaviors, habits and more. Although shifting may sound simple, it's not easy. It requires a willingness to set aside our most guarded beliefs and conclusions and see ourselves in a more expansive light. For example, imagine you are standing near a blazing bonfire. Notice the way you perceive the event occurring before you. The normal way of seeing the fire is to notice the *flame*. This object-oriented perception is based on looking for, and identifying, *nouns*. In other words, you are looking at a *thing* called *flame*, which is a progression of other things, such as *heat, cinders, wood* and *smoke*. Although a valid means of perception, it is only one of many ways to perceive reality.

Shifting to another perspective requires expanding perception beyond the dimension of *flame* to the dimension of *flaming*. From this expanded perspective, we now can recognize the *verb* attributes of the fire in addition to its *noun* attributes. Seeing in terms of verb allows us to more fully recognize the movement and process of what occurs. From this perspective, we are able to see *into* the flaming, noticing not just the flame but also the multiple, constantly shifting ribbons of light and energy dancing together. Although they are still one *flame*, they also share a common flaming or burn zone. Now, rather than only having one dimension of knowing, we have two. The unique aspect of the *Light of the Masters* is that it illuminates seven dimensions of knowing, each adding to the cumulative power of the other, exponentially increasing our wisdom.

I wouldn't be too concerned at this point about understanding the *Light of the Masters* or multidimensional perspectives. This book will act as a personal guide and lead you directly into the burn zone of your own life. If you stay with it, the sevenfold wisdom of the *Light of the Masters* will be revealed to you. I say "if you stay with it" because there is a challenge to embarking on this soulful sojourn. The domain of the *Master's Light* is called a "burn zone" for good reason. As I recount my experiences for you, I suspect we will travel in tandem to the inner dimensions of our minds and souls. Imagine you and I are about to climb a mountain or explore a dense jungle together. As we travel into this inner landscape, you will most likely find yourself delving into the depths of yourself and reflecting on many facets of your own life. Because these reflections reach deeply into vulnerable aspects of human nature, they can cause substantial heat. The ensuing "burning" sheds the "default" perspectives and antiquated beliefs that shroud the *Light of the Masters*. Once these shrouds are burned away, an expansive vision and multidimensional wisdom becomes illuminated.

As we travel into the burn zone of the *Inca Fire*, we must be willing to embrace the full spectrum of emotions, thoughts and feelings that arise. If we limit what we are willing to experience, we may never reach the wisdom we seek; however, it's not all rough terrain. The further we move into the burn zone, the easier the journey becomes; we gain greater clarity and become more inspired. We discover why certain events occurred in our lives and begin to see the larger meaning for why things happened as they did. In fact, we adopt a powerful perspective that will endure *anything* that ever befalls us—a perspective of sacredness and resilience. The scholar and poet Ralph Waldo Emerson spoke of this perspective in his treatise *The Oversoul:*

> Behold, it saith, I am born into the great, the universal mind. I, the imperfect, adore my own Perfect. I am somehow receptive of the great soul, and thereby I do overlook the sun and the stars and feel them to be the fair accidents and effects which change and pass. More and more the surges of everlasting nature enter into me, and I become public and human in my regards and actions. So come I to live in thoughts and act with energies which are immortal. Thus revering the soul, and learning, as the ancient said, that 'its beauty is immense,' man will come to see that the world is the perennial miracle which the soul worketh, and be less astonished at particular wonders; he will learn that there is no profane history; that all history is sacred.

Not only will we develop deeper understanding of the sacredness of life by traveling into the burn zone together, but with each sojourn into the "flames," we will also reestablish and strengthen our connection with our own soul. When the power of our soul is available to us, it provides us with resilience, faith and an awareness that we are far more capable than we may have believed.

I'd like to clarify a few points before we begin. Although the title of this book is *"Inca Fire!"* it's not necessary to have an interest in or understanding of the Inca civilization to gain value from it. Additionally, although many of the stories I recount may be considered "masculine challenges," I assure my female readers that gender is of no consequence. Regarding the book's content, no matter how extreme or wild my stories may seem, every one of them is true. Every memory, recollection and experience I write about happened just as I describe it. The "travel log" portions of the book, where I trace my journey through Peru, are also accurate in terms of the sequence of events and the experiences I had along the way. I recorded all key events as they happened so I could recount them accurately. Whatever was not recorded, I tried to recall with as much authenticity as possible.

Throughout the book you will also find sections that have been italicized and indented to set them apart from my other writings. These sections contain what I believe to be inspired messages I received while at the ruins of Machu Picchu. I say *inspired* because of the mysterious manner in which they were delivered to me and because of the remarkable insights they produced. Manifesting as lucid dreams and realistic visions, the messages included visual images, auditory stimuli and a variety of strange body sensations. The visuals included multicolored flames, human faces of Inca priests and priestesses, deities, and a variety of indigenous animals. Some visions seemed more real than others. For example, there were instances when I saw what looked like flames raging before me and not only could I see the fire, I could feel its heat as well. Other times, I got a mere glimpse of something: a bird's wing, a face, a flash of light, or a fleeting shadow. Each time a vision came to me, I felt compelled to write down phrases and passages that literally popped into my head, similar to automatic writing. Sometimes only a few words or phrases came to me. Other times, whole passages flowed uninterrupted and without reflection or intervention on my part.

You might be saying to yourself, "Well, well, another guy who channels high frequency metaphysics." Allow me to clarify. Although the messages I received were inspired, I don't think they were channeled or metaphysical. My feeling is that anyone who opens up to the wonders of the world, to the incredible mystery of nature or even the innocent beauty of a child, can receive inspired information.

Unlike *The Celestine Prophecy,* by James Redfield, and *The Way of the Peaceful Warrior,* by Dan Millman, *Inca Fire* is a true story. Any similarity between my work and theirs is purely coincidental, as I did not model my content or the motif of my book after them. From my experience, in matters of human development and spiritual evolution, there is a common set of principles that unites the myriad of different religions, faiths and practices of the world. These common principles have been written about from time immemorial and, I hope, will continue to be the focus of scholars and seekers alike.

The last point is that I have been a high-risk explorer for many years, and thereby have accumulated some extreme and uncommon experiences. Just because some of the experiences I share in this book are extreme, it doesn't make them any more spiritual than common occurrences a person may have in their day-to-day life. In fact, it has been my observation that ordinary experiences often possess the greatest blessings. As you travel into your own burn zone, it is important that you not compare *your* life experiences to mine, or anyone else's for that matter. Every person's life is unique and filled with its own special wisdom. Having said that, let me now introduce you to a mystical land, where both the extreme and the common coexist within a blazing burn zone of Inca wisdom.

Val Jon Farris

Wayna Picchu standing behind cloud vapor—calling to those who aspire to climb to its majestic and sacred summit.

FOREWORD

THE LOST CIVILIZATION OF THE INCAS

Shrouded from the civilized world for more than five hundred years, the lost civilization of Machu Picchu crowns the Peruvian Andes with an enigmatic splendor. Built by the Incas around the fifteenth century, the isolated city of Machu Picchu is embraced on the north by the watershed of the Wakay Willka mountain range, on the east and west by the Sacred Urubamba Valley, and on the south by the ridge line of the Salcantay Mountains. The peaks of these great Andes range from fifteen thousand feet to over twenty thousand feet in elevation. The Urubamba River, which flows gently around the base of the ancient mountains, lies at an elevation of fifty-six hundred feet. Like ancient stone daggers lining the gorges, monolithic peaks rise up out of the Sacred Valley into the heavens.

Hand carved out of the granite topped ridge of one of these monoliths, Machu Picchu is a labyrinth of mind boggling rock stairways, grassy terraces, roofless stone structures and mystical altars. Its architectural design is consistent with the Inca cosmology of "complementary opposites," with the agricultural sector at the higher part of the ridge and the urban sector in the lower part. The urban sector is further subdivided into the "Hanan" or upper half and "Hurin," lower half. Most of the ceremonial architecture, including the Principal Temple, the Temple of Three Windows and the Intiwatana Altar, are positioned in the upper half. Where the Hanan and the Hurin halves overlap is a large public square called the Central Plaza, which resembles a football field. In this shared space community activities, ceremonial events and social gatherings took place.

Machu Picchu's inhabitants, the Inca, were a profoundly spiritual race. Mystical forces ruled their existence and inspired them to weave together both the mundane and the miraculous into a colorful tapestry of everyday worship. The focus of their daily devotion included honoring agricultural and celestial cycles and venerating the natural world. The Inca held a cosmic vision that nature and time are a single living entity infusing life and vitality into both animate and inanimate objects, which in turn provide mankind with inspiration through the medium of spirits and deities. High priests and shamans were said to possess magical powers that linked man, nature, animals and the Gods together into one symbiotic organism. The mountains and rivers, sun and moon, rocks, plants and animals were all believed to house deities with whom the Inca communicated. As legend has it, the worship of these deities endowed the Inca with powers to bestow blessings or curses on those within their sphere of influence.

Unlike the lore of the Mayans, who organized their civilization around temples of war and sacrificial altars, the Incas constructed Machu Picchu as a sanctuary for the cultivation of wisdom, peace and communal harmony. The name "Machu Picchu," in its oldest definition, means "Old Bird" and refers to the Peruvian Condor, which brought peace to the Inca people and supposedly transported their souls to the land of their ancestors. Yet for reasons still unknown, its inhabitants abandoned their community of peace a mere eighty years after its establishment. Remarkably, many parts of the city were still under construction when the Incas vacated. Even stranger yet, archeologists have established that the Inca's evacuation was immediate rather than gradual. Evidence shows that they made a sudden withdrawal from the city, taking their belongings with them as they fled. Speculation has it that a severe drought forced them out. Still others say that rebel tribes from the nearby city of Vilcabamba pillaged and burned Machu Picchu to create a "scorched earth" zone between themselves and the Spanish conquistadors, to prevent them from discovering access routes through the Andes.

According to Andean priests living in Aguas Calientes, a small village nestled at the base of the mountain which holds the Machu Picchu ruins, none of these explanations are true. They say that the Gods became displeased and intentionally struck Machu Picchu with lightning, terrorizing its inhabitants and compelling them to flee. Legend tells of a high priest who for decades provided the community with spiritual guidance and social stability. One day he suddenly fell sick and died. After his death, the Inca people began to experiment with dark forces, sorcery and black magic. The more they engaged in these irreverent acts, the angrier the Gods became. One night, during a wild pagan festival the Gods struck with terrible force. A gigantic blinding bolt of fire raged down from above, slamming into the hillside supporting the Principal Temple and vaporizing masses of stone, earth and flesh. (When I examined the ruins, it was apparent that parts of the temple wall and sections of the mountainside it stood on were clearly missing). Feeling the wrath of the Gods and believing that Machu Picchu had been cursed, the survivors fled, vowing never to return and never to speak of the place again.

The vow of silence seems to have been fulfilled as Machu Picchu remained lost to the world for more than five centuries. The secrecy was finally broken on July 24, 1911, when an explorer from Yale University named Hiram Bingham had been told about the ruins by natives and sought out the site. He could see a little of Machu Picchu, covered by a tropical jungle, but as he moved deeper into the overgrown foliage, he was spellbound by what he found. Never in all his life had he seen such remarkable works of stone. Since that day, people from all over the world have been enchanted by the sacred mystical sanctuary.

At the age of nineteen, I, too, became spellbound by Machu Picchu. Something about it called to me. I was compelled to pore over all the available pictures, documents and film footage I could find. I vowed that someday I would stand upon its sacred ground, experience its witchery and maybe even connect with the Gods who had supposedly cast down that fateful and blinding bolt of lightning. Little did I know that I would not only connect with these Gods one day, but would find myself stepping directly into the burn zone of the *Inca Fire*.

CHAPTER ONE

THE SEAT OF THE CONDOR

The Seat of the Condor holds the eyes of the sky
As they view timeless terraces and humble souls
And still they hold Inca passion with a mighty cry
For eternity knows no bounds, nor do I
In the Seat of the Condor above the sky

Surfacing in a shadowy crevice between three colossal granite boulders, I scan their smooth surfaces for a foothold. The sun is sinking fast over the western ridge, making light scarce. There must be a way to gain access to the summit. The ancients who founded this place centuries ago surely forged an ascent route, but where is it?

Think like Inca climbers. What would *they* do? The smell of damp granite and rich moss permeates my senses as I lean back against rigid stone. In a moment absent of thought, the answer suddenly comes. Peering into the darkness, I notice a small stone step in front of one of the massive boulders. Using the stone as a springboard, I catapult myself upward. Scaling the angular edge of the rock I slowly work my way to its topside. As I rise to my feet, legs shaking from exhaustion, a rush of exhilaration fills me. I am standing on the summit of Wayna Picchu, a massive pinnacle of granite rising two thousand feet above the northern edge of the Machu Picchu ruins. Pearl-white clouds fill the valley far below as

1

the sun's golden rays illuminate them like divine ethereal lampshades. Vibrant blue skies showcase the majestic peaks of the Peruvian Andes. Translucent shadows creep across ancient stone faces, casting a mysterious glow upon the earth's rugged brow. In the distance, two condors soar through spires of granite as they weave their way between the majesty of heaven and the beauty of earth.

To the south and far below lay the ancient ruins of Machu Picchu. From my perspective high on the summit they look like a huge bird carved into the top of a mountainous ridge. The terraced agricultural slopes make up its feathered wings, the mosaic of temples and roofless structures its body, and the old Inca trail entering the site from the high south its outstretched claws. As I scan the structures within the ancient civilization, the sun's rays stream horizontally across the valley, piercing rare air with an array of translucent ribbons of light. The shadows of night slowly engulf the visible world, as they edge their way up ancient slopes. The wind whispers its secrets—invisible streams of wisdom only audible from such a high place as this. My effort, strife and exhaustion from the climb pale in contrast to what my eyes, my heart and my soul are now witnessing. I am at total peace.

The boulder beneath my feet is the second highest on the summit. To the north, just a few feet away, it merges with a small pinnacle that rises three feet higher. To the south, it gently rises and flattens to an oblong slab with a surface approximately six feet by ten feet. In the fading light, I make out a jagged pattern of white granite shards with gray edges sweeping up the slab toward its far edge, which converges into an elevated circular crater. I move closer to investigate. The crater looks like it's been hand carved in the rock. The back edge flares up to a peak, giving it the appearance of a bird's pointed beak. Around the rim of the indentation, small flat spots look like ledges for candles or offerings. Its six-inch-deep inner surface is perfectly curved, like a seat.

Crouching next to it, I reach for a spot in the center of its inner curve. The moment I make contact I feel a strange sensation in the pit of my stomach. What happens next stuns me. Visions of blazing red and yellow flames burst into my mind. Deep within the flames, faces twist and contort in the movement of the fire. Peering deeper into the light, I make out the faces of wise men and women, chiefs, natives and priests. Some of them have braided hair, others are wearing red and black face paint and narrow multicolored headbands. The faces are both young and old, and all appear to be of Inca descent. Their high cheekbones, dark skin and wise eyes are much like those of the native people I've encountered throughout Peru. As I remove my hand from the crater, the faces slowly recede into the flames and the flames vaporize into the cool clear air.

Rocking back on my heels, I shake my head and balance myself by thrusting the fingers of my left hand down to the stone slab. Were the images just figments of my imagination, or were they real? They weren't tangible flesh and blood, so they couldn't have been physical, yet the flames and the faces were so vivid they seemed real. Whatever they were, they made a profound impression on me. What kind of place is this? Have I been drawn to some kind of shrine or ancient ceremonial altar? My musings are suddenly eclipsed by a swiftly moving shadow. I spot a large black-winged bird overhead. Its holds me in its piercing gaze as it soars clockwise above me. It's similar to a raven in size and color, but the trailing-edge feathers of its wings are more uneven than a raven's. Also, its beak is fuller and has a stunning black lacquer sheen. As suddenly as the bird appeared, it vanishes.

I close my eyes and feel the subtle movement of turbulent air around my face. Although the bird had a black ominous look, it felt lighthearted and gracious. It seemed to relay acceptance and welcome to me. My body is at ease and my breathing is steady. I slowly open my eyes and it's there above, circling me again, this time in a counterclockwise direction. There is something strange about the bird—something ancient and wise—something urgent, yet mysteriously intentional. Peering up into its glimmering eye these words suddenly come to me:

Come sit in this high place, the Seat of the Condor, for here are the eyes of the sky.

The Seat of the Condor? Looking down at the stone indentation, suddenly it makes sense. It *is* a seat of some kind. The circular crater is just the right size to sit in and its back edge appears to be a perfect backrest. This must be some kind of altar. The Inca were known to engage in spiritual rituals that enabled them to commune with animal deities. This altar could be some kind of deity-link to the Peruvian Condors. Although the bird flying above me is too small to be a condor, it could be some kind of messenger. (I found out later from an Andean priest that this species of bird is known as an emissary of the Condor, the spirit bird that acts as an intermediary between the world of the living and the souls of the dead.)

Taking the cue to sit, I ease my backside into the smooth curved indentation and lean back against its solid stone rim. I feel like a king or a high priest sitting here. I immediately get that strange sensation in the pit of my stomach again. Red and yellow flames suddenly burst forth in my mind and within them the same ancient faces I saw earlier begin to materialize. Fixing my gaze directly into the middle of the mysterious flames, another message comes:

In your soul, and in the soul of all those who have ever been, are, or shall ever be, the Light of the Masters burns as an eternal fire. Hidden like a brilliant light beneath layers of history, sadness, joy, love and pain, its sevenfold nature waits to be revealed. The "light" is expressed as Seven Dimensions of Knowing: Humility, Eternality, Truth, Passion, Sovereignty, Faith and Service. Each is forged within the Inca Fire like gems deep within the earthstone. When revealed and embraced, they endow the soul with divine insight and wisdom.

The full moon high in the eastern sky provides just enough light to record the philosophical words in my spiral-bound notebook. The yellowish lunar glow illuminates the passage as I read it over and over again trying to understand its meaning. Each of the terms within the "seven dimensions of knowing" is familiar to me, but their "sevenfold nature" doesn't make much sense. Little do I know I am in for a night filled with insights and realizations that will illuminate the specific meanings of each dimension as well as the collective power of their sevenfold nature. I pick up my pen again as I feel another message coming. It will be the first of seven incredible insights that will lead me directly into the burn zone of the *Inca Fire*.

And so the Light of the Masters reveals the first dimension called Humility, which holds ever present reflections through space and time and sky and clouds—to be in your presence—reminding me of my origin and home—encouraging me to dance and shine my way into life. Humility itself has no form, its presence is invisible to the naked eye. It is visible only to the naked soul and the humble heart, which ever longs for the light yet still beats with undying devotion within the body, never seeing the light of day. Inside this earthstone, too, is darkness filled with the Light of the Masters. May solids hold together ever densely for us to stand upon as they emanate the light through their crystal gemlike forms.

The vision of flames is now all around me. Between the ribbons of fire I notice areas of shadowy darkness. The contrast between rich red and yellow flames and these stark gaping holes of darkness produces an eerie paradoxical hotbed of illumination. Studying the darkness more closely, I can see it's not just shadows but rather portals or tunnels of some kind. My head spins and my heart pumps madly. I try closing my eyes but the vision pierces my eyelids. What is happening to me? Am I hallucinating? Am I delirious or making this up? I know in my mind that what is going on can't be real, but it *looks* and *feels* so real! Suddenly, one of the portals grows to an immense size. I am welded to the Seat of the Condor and cannot move a muscle. In terror, I emotionally brace myself as the darkness consumes me. Sucked into a vacuous flux of light and darkness, my mind shatters into a million fragments. Awareness, reflections and memories splinter off into oblivion. Fighting to stay conscious, I command myself to focus on something, on *anything* that will give me a sense of certainty. As I struggle, chaotic fragments begin to cohere, like a scattered liquid mosaic reforming into a unified picture—a picture that will cast me into my past and illuminate the awesome power of *Humility*.

CHAPTER TWO

HUMILITY:

THE FIRST DIMENSION OF KNOWING

Make humble this heart and reverent this soul
That I may reflect in the shadow of my maker
and dance in the light of her grace

"Why don't *you* get up and make the coffee, while *I* stay here in bed and plan the climb?" I ask Henk hopefully. He just looks at me with that unassuming, *give-me-a-break-Val Jon* look of his. The year is 1987 and my friend Henk and I had just spent four months preparing for our climb to the top of Mount Shasta. Of South African descent, Henk stands a wiry six foot two, has short blond hair and is in substantially better shape than I am for this climb. He has a colonial British accent that makes me feel pleasantly calm when he speaks. Henk is a man of integrity and kindness, one of the most lighthearted and cheerful guys I've ever known.

It's three o'clock in the morning, cold, dark and damp, and neither of us wants to get out of our sleeping bags. But we're committed to this climb, so we don our parkas and gloves and confront the chill of the morning. As we huddle around the tiny butane stove, we reflect on the sequence of events that led us to climb this 14,162-foot mountain.

Henk pours the contents of a small packet into the tiny coffee pot and says, "Val Jon, why do you think people decide to climb mountains?"

Out of my frozen and blistered lips comes, "More important Henk, why do some people change their minds?"

Somehow the laughter subdues the flood of second thoughts filling our minds. It was common knowledge that about five thousand people attempt to climb Mount Shasta every year, yet less than half make it to the top.

Our laughter is suddenly broken by the climb director's gruff voice, "Everybody gather round and listen up!" Thirty-three sober faces are illuminated by dancing firelight as the climb director ominously announces, "In a few hours, we will begin our ascent of the west face of Shasta, and it requires all of us to work together. As you all know, this climb is dangerous. Many have died on this mountain. There have been various causes, but one cause has taken more lives than any other: the dead thought they could do it alone." The message casts a chill of reality through the climb team.

After we finish breaking camp, Henk and I lay back on a large rock and gaze up into the heavens. The mountain's black silhouette eclipses half our view, revealing a sharp contrast between the emptiness of space and the density of the earth. At an elevation of over ten thousand feet, there are more stars than sky, and as I look up into the heavens I feel more connected to the earth than I have ever been. It's so strange. On one hand, I'm nervous about the challenge ahead, and on the other, I'm busting with excitement and enthusiasm. From deep down inside a rush of emotion fills me with the awareness that I love this planet and everything on it. In silence I reach down, scoop up a handful of soil, and then watch it slowly fall through my fingers. I lift my fingers to my face and inhale deeply. What an incredible smell this dirt has. As far back as I can remember, even as a boy, the earth has always had the same rich, dense, primal smell. Remarkably, the earth has always been here to support me. No matter where I have stood, it has always, always been here to hold me up.

"Wonderful, isn't it?" Henk asks.

"Yes, it sure is," I whisper.

I remember the moment, months ago, when I committed to climbing this mountain. I had actually considered not doing it, because I wasn't an experienced climber. As I lie here now though, looking up into the heavens, I am grateful that I chose to go through with it. It took a lot of effort and work just to get to the base camp of Lake Helen at 10,400 feet. I spent months training and preparing for the expedition and pushed myself far beyond what I thought I was capable of. As first light breaks over the rim of the earth, I have a simple but enlightening insight. The key to self-appreciation is in doing something worthy of appreciation.

Without speaking, Henk and I stand up in unison, gather our gear, and join the rest of the team to prepare for our ascent of the icy slopes. The full moon casts a bluish light over the face of the steep glacier, creating a moonlike ambiance. The eerie silence and otherworldly terrain evoke both awe-filled eyes and iron wills. This will be a treacherous climb and we'll need to be vigilant. One stupid act could cast our fates and end our lives. Because of the vertical slope and the open fractures in the ice, we decide not to rope together; instead we'll stay in proximity and zigzag our way up the mountain.

Ice climbing typically requires crampons for the boots and ice axes for leverage and braking. The climb we are about to embark on, the steep ascent of Avalanche Gulch, requires such gear. It's especially dangerous because of the high number of fissures and the glazed surface of the ice. Glazed ice makes traction difficult and braking even harder. Braking is used exclusively when a climber loses his footing and falls on steep terrain. It's done by grabbing the axe with both hands, flipping onto one's side and plunging the axe into the ice as an anchor. Keeping the axe close to the body helps maintain control and increases the anchor depth. Everyone on the team has practiced the procedure many times and can deploy it without hesitation if they need to.

"We're going to ascend in groups of seven and work our way up the left side of the glacier," says our climb director.

Just ahead, we spot a huge deep fissure in the ice. We move cautiously around its left edge and then cross back ten or twelve feet above it. Climbing to the center of the open slope, we weave our way back to the left to gain altitude and distance from the abyss. All goes well until I traverse back to the left edge of the glacier. The crampon on my left boot suddenly pops loose from my boot and I lose my footing. Tumbling headfirst into space, I instinctively grab my axe with both hands to prepare to brake. Landing hard on my back, the axe bounces loose from my hands and I slide down the ice in sheer terror. I am going to die!

I abruptly smash into something solid, and the wind is knocked out of me. Blinded by snow, unable to breathe, I am helpless. Looking up, I see a blur of movement and shifting dark images. I soon realize that Henk and my fellow climbers have formed a human net, catching me just before I career over the edge of the abyss! I'm stunned and speechless. I'm also embarrassed and feeling extremely vulnerable. I have spent years being independent, never needing anybody. Needing help always seems like a sign of weakness, so this accident is deeply disturbing for me.

"We've got ya! Hold on, we're not gonna let you fall!"

"Thanks everybody, I can take it from here," I respond.

"Lie still, you're pushing us back into the crevasse!" Henk barks at me.

"No, really, I'm okay now. I can deal with it."

"Stop wiggling around, damn it! Let us help you. You're gonna push us over the edge if you don't stop," another climber shouts.

Finally getting the message, I relax and let them reattach my crampon and straighten my gear. As they stand me up and reassure me, I realize it is almost impossible for people to support me. Suddenly tears come to my eyes as I see how many times in my life I have not let others help me. I would always say, "No problem, I can do it myself." I didn't want to burden anyone or put anyone out. Most of all, I worried that if I let someone support me, I would be obligated to them in the future. Looking into the caring faces of my climbing partners, however, I see superimposed images of family members, friends and past relationships that I had alienated with my stubborn independence. I reflect on the pain and frustration that not being able to help me must have caused them.

Standing here among my fellow climbers I realize that I have a choice: I can hide behind my rugged armor, or I can open myself to their concern and love. I choose to open up, and as I do, a flood of emotion fills me. For the first time in my life I am able to see that accepting help from someone is not a sign of weakness, but rather a demonstration of humility. I also realize that rather than being a burden and a drag on people when I am in need, it allows others to feel worthwhile through offering support. There is no doubt that my fellow climbers are ecstatic about having just saved my life. My armor of rugged individualism is finally cracking and falling way. I now understand that being open and accepting support is a very important part of life. It doesn't mean I'm weak, it simply means I'm human.

"Let's try it again, everybody," our climb director announces. "We've got to reach the summit by one o'clock or we won't have time to descend to base camp before dark."

Without delay or further incident, we climb toward the peak. Surviving a steep section of ice called Misery Hill, we arrive only a few hundred yards from the summit. It's just high noon now, so we have plenty of time. All thirty-three of us gather together near a sulfur hot spring and discuss how we will proceed to the top. Excitement and the smell of rotten eggs permeate thin cool air. Slowly but surely each group makes its way to the top until all of us are sitting in a semicircle on the snow-covered summit. A crystalline blue sky embraces the curve of the earth as a light flurry of snow dances on rare air. Shining, sunburned faces grin from ear to ear in a blissful exchange of laughter and tears. My face, especially open and especially thankful, beams with appreciation and enthusiasm.

After celebrating our accomplishment, we begin the ritual of reading and signing the register book that rests atop most climbable mountains in the world. The register book is used by climbers to express personal insights and record dedications. Each member of our team, like those before us, takes the opportunity to write a personal note. After finishing his, Henk passes the old, weathered book to me. I flip through the yellowed pages and my eyes fall on a paragraph written October 23, 1972. I'll never forget what it said:

> I dedicate this climb to you, Father. I am standing at the top of Mount Shasta today because of the love and encouragement and support you gave me as I was growing up. It is through your undying commitment and dedication to me as your son that I am able to view the beauty before me. And although you lost your legs in the Korean War and have never been able to stand beside me, Dad, I want you to know that today I stand on the top of this mountain for both of us. I love you with all my heart and all my soul, your son John.

I close the register book, stand up slowly and walk to the edge of the summit. As I take in the grandeur of the earth's curve, I weep in silence. In this moment, humility is fully revealed to me. I stand here clutching the register book to my chest, feeling compassion for *all* the world's fathers, sons, mothers and daughters. I feel intrinsically connected to everyone on this earth. I am a family member of the human race, worthy of our greatest deeds and equally guilty of our worst crimes. For many years I held myself separate from those I judged, as if I were not part of the human race, but in this moment, I realize that another's deeds are a reflection of *my* character because they are part of *my* family. I may not agree with what they do, and I may not understand their culture, but as a member of the human race, I humbly share in the responsibility for all our actions.

Reading more pages from the register book, I realize these inspiring expressions come from a place of deep humility.

Dedication after dedication points to a profound sense of relatedness. On the way back down the mountain, I reflect on my life and sense that this quality of relatedness is lacking in society, in business, and in our families. Although I can't change the world, I can do my part to bring a measure of humility into my life, and maybe into the lives of people I touch and with whom I interact. Where I need humility most, however, is with my own family. I haven't spoken to my father for more than fifteen years because I didn't like the way he raised me, and over the years my disdain and judgment had increased. If I truly intend to take humility to heart, I must demonstrate it—and the demonstration will be more challenging than climbing any mountain could ever be.

I am so inspired by the events that occurred on Mount Shasta that a day after descending I call my father. It's one of those calls where part of me wants to connect, but another part hopes to God he doesn't answer. *Ring, ring, ring . . .*

"Hello?"

"Hello, Dad it's your son Val."

"Val! I haven't talked with you in years. Are you in trouble?"

"No. No, Dad, I'm not in any trouble."

"You need money, right? How much do you need?"

"No. No, that's not why I'm calling."

"Well then, why are you calling?"

"Dad, I'm calling because I love you and I want our relationship back. I've realized that although I didn't care for the way you raised me, I didn't need to be so arrogant with you and alienate you the way I did. I want you to know I'm sorry for that and I also want you to know that I love you very much."

There is a long silence on the other end of the phone and then he breaks down and weeps. My heart falls through the floor as I listen to his response.

"Son, I want you to know I've been in hell for many years over what I did to you, your brother and sister and your mother. I've learned a great deal over the years and have made many amends in my life. Can you ever forgive me for what I did?"

13

Now the silence is on my end. My throat constricts as I grapple with his question. It is so hard to forgive someone, especially when we have invested so much in judging them over the years. But if I'm going to live true to the meaning of humility I must open up and allow myself to forgive him. I have to make a very important decision at this point. Am I more interested in proving how wrong he had been, or am I interested in resurrecting our relationship? I can't have both; one or the other will have to go. Which will it be? Is it more valuable to me to hold onto all the wrongs he had done, or will I let them go and humbly reach out to him?

"Dad, I do forgive you. Although I don't like some of the things that happened between us as I was growing up, I do forgive you and I love you."

My response to him was freeing for both of us. We reminisced, talked about old times, good and bad, but discussed them all openly and honestly. I should also point out that I wasn't a model child. I pulled a number of stunts that would push any parent over the edge.

One of the most important things I learned during our exchange was that the humility I gained on the mountaintop enabled me to forgive my father for the way he treated me as I was growing up. As we talked, a sense of affinity grew between us. We laughed and cried about old times and even bantered back and forth in playful jest. Our history of separation was over. We were father and son again.

From this experience I learned that humility can't happen unless I am open to it. If I'm unwilling to release my negative conclusions about someone, I can't expect the relationship to work. I'm either committed to being right and looking for evidence to prove my case or doing something to resurrect what has gone bad. One of the hardest things in the world to do is to let go of grudges and negative conclusions, but the fact of the matter is, they don't serve anyone's best interest. In fact, when we hold negative thoughts about others, it is only ourselves who wind up suffering.

As my memory fades I find myself back at the Seat of the Condor. The full moon is beaming down around me, casting shadows over this ancient sanctuary. The *Inca Fire* had transported me back more than ten years into my past, and although I had often reflected on my Mount Shasta climb and the heart-to-heart talk with my father, I now realize something very important: it's not only the inspiration I gained from my mountain climb that brought humility into my life, it's the inspiration coupled with the courage to actually call my father and deal with the issue that solidified humility within me. If I hadn't acted on my inspiration, my experience of humility would soon have dissipated.

I stand up, stretch my legs, and look out over the moonlit landscape, down to the ruins far below. If the experience I just had with humility was any indicator of the power of the *Light of the Masters*, I hope I will again get the chance to step into this remarkable "burn zone."

The Seat of the Condor atop the Wayna Picchu summit, two thousand feet above the ruins of Machu Picchu.

CHAPTER THREE

FROM LIMA TO CUSCO

Tiny Inca eyes shining wide
now fast emptying out dreams and mysteries
onto parched and bruised ground
Here is my hand, that I may reach down
with compassion and say, come child,
I celebrate you and I honor your being

Passporto por favor?" The dark-skinned inspector waves his hand in sync with his Peruvian accent as he motions me forward. I reach into my tattered black backpack and fumble blindly for my passport. Normally I'm more prepared when it comes to moments like this, but I'm preoccupied with the strange ambiance of Lima, Peru. I sift through my overstuffed pack, finally feeling the document tucked between my paperback travel guide and my wire-rimmed sunglasses. Extracting it hastily, I slide it down onto the worn metal-topped immigration desk.

The inspector's greasy hair protrudes from both sides of his faded blue military cap as he scrutinizes my photo. Suddenly I have that familiar sinking feeling that I get whenever I enter a third world country. It's the "Am I gonna wind up in prison with toothless derelicts and corrupt cigar-smoking guards for the rest of my life?" feeling. Even with nothing to hide and nothing to declare, paranoia reigns. The young male security guard standing at the end of the immigration counter and packing a submachine gun may have something to do with my feelings of insecurity.

"All part of the journey," I say to myself. And what a journey this has become. The anticipation of finally seeing Machu Picchu fills my every waking moment. In a few more days I will be standing at one of the most mystical civilizations ever built.

Thwap! Thwap! Two sharp thumps onto my passport with the inspector's approval stamp shatter my daydream. Stuffing the stricken document into my pack, I make my way through the security gate and turn back to see if my traveling partner, Alberto, will escape the administrative tyranny as well. The familiar sound of the approval stamp smacking hard on Alberto's passport assures me that all is well. In a roundabout way, Alberto is partially responsible for me realizing my dream of visiting Machu Picchu. He had attended one of my corporate leadership workshops in Miami, Florida a few months earlier, and subsequently sponsored me to come to Brazil to conduct the program for managers within his organization. Of Jewish descent, Alberto stands just over six feet tall, has a goatee, thinning dark hair, heavy rimmed glasses and a soft, childlike appearance. In his early fifties, he could be taken for just about any nationality south of the equator. Alberto is a kind and gentle soul who is soft-spoken, and yet when he speaks, there is always a ring of passion in his words. Seldom have I met someone who has such appreciation and love for life.

As we exit the immigration counter, Alberto has a tranquil and knowing look on his face. "Very good," he whispers, "we are still free men, no?" Past the security station, we approach the main terminal. The Lima airport looks more like a penal colony than an airline lobby. The drab gray, green and yellow two-story interior with its open fluorescent bulb lights, coupled with the presence of heavily armed militia creates an eerie, prison-like atmosphere.

Lima, the capital of Peru, is an overcrowded and polluted metropolis inhabited by over eight million people. Located on the drought-stricken eastern coast of South America, it has not had rain in over thirty years. As a result, a thick, gray smog blinds the city nearly year round. Lima means "city of kings," and was founded by Francisco Pizarro in 1535. The city grew rapidly and became the seat for the Spanish Inquisition in 1569. A disastrous earthquake leveled most of Lima in 1746, and consequently most of its colonial architecture has vanished.

"I feel like a stranger in a strange land, Alberto."

"What is theeze, 'strange land,' Val Jon?" he asks, in a broken English accent.

"It comes from a popular book called *Stranger in a Strange Land* that talks about how some people feel out of place because they know they are from a different time or place."

"Hmmm," he responds quietly.

There's some magic involved in Alberto and I making this pilgrimage together. After completing our leadership workshop, Alberto and his wife Rosa invited me to a social gathering at their home in Brazil. They had also invited fifteen or twenty other guests with the intent that we might contribute to each other and possibly network together. The party had taken place just a few days prior to our departure for Peru. The gathering turned out to be a pivotal event, setting the tone and direction for the incredible journey about to unfold.

"Val Jon, I'd like you to meet Eliceu. Eliceu is my meditation teacher," Alberto announces as he motions us closer together.

"Hello, Eliceu. I'm pleased to meet you."

"Hello to you, Val Jon. It's very good to meet you, my friend."

In a flash, I pick up the "my friend" part of his greeting. Everyone I have met in Brazil has had a remarkable warmth and immediate ability to create a relationship. Even though I have never met him, Eliceu feels comfortable in extending a measure of friendship to me. I feel welcomed and appreciated.

Eliceu stands just over six feet tall, has a medium build, short but thick black hair and a young, rounded face with warm, brown Brazilian eyes. In his early thirties, he possesses a soothing smile that communicates safety and peace. As we spend time talking together at the party, I experience his rich character, which is filled with lighthearted humility, great intelligence and a sense of grace.

"Will you be staying long in Brazil, Val Jon?" Eliceu asks.

"I'm leaving tomorrow for Iguacu Falls and then to Peru."

"Peru? What will you be doing in Peru?"

"I'm going to visit the ruins at Machu Picchu."

"Really? I, too, will be in Machu Picchu next week."

"No kidding. When will you be there?" I ask.

"On July 9," he replies.

"July 9! That's when I'm going to be there."

"Val Jon, do you know that July 9 is a very special night at Machu Picchu?"

"No. I wasn't aware of anything special about it. What's the deal?"

"The deal?" he asks quizzically, tilting his head slightly.

"Sorry, Eliceu. It's an English slang word that means, what will be going on that's so special?"

"The ninth of July is a very special night at Machu Picchu. There is a group called Paux Universal, the Church of Universal Peace, whose members will converge there from all over the world for a spiritual ceremony."

"What kind of spiritual ceremony?"

"Rumor through the metaphysical community is that on the eve of the ninth, the full moon will trigger the opening of a "gate" into the ethereal heavens and the *Light of the Masters* will be revealed to those who witness it."

"The *Light of the Masters*? What do you know about this phenomenon, Eliceu?"

"I know little, but my sense is that it will be an opportunity to tap into some kind of ancient wisdom or knowledge."

"Do you plan on joining the church group for the ceremony?" I ask.

"I'm hosting one of my own for some of my meditation students that evening, so I'll be in a different section of the ruins; however, I will be very attentive to this 'gate' to be sure."

"Eliceu, this is amazing. Since I was a young man I have wanted to visit Machu Picchu. It has been a lifelong dream, and to be there on a night like this couldn't be more perfect."

"No accident, yes, Val Jon?"

"No accident to be sure, my friend."

"We must plan on meeting on the ninth, don't you agree?"

"Certainly. Where will you be staying, Eliceu?"

"I'll be at the Pueblo Hotel in Aguas Calientes near the base of Machu Picchu. It's one of the inns built next to the Urubamba River."

"Doesn't the Santa Ana train run next to the Urubamba Gorge and intersect Aguas Calientes at some point?"

"Yes. It's about a four-hour rail ride from Cusco to Aguas Calientes and then only a short walk to the Pueblo Hotel."

"I'll look you up early in the day on the ninth, and perhaps we'll get together."

"Sounds very good Val Jon. I'll see you there my friend."

Alberto listened to every word and almost fell off his chair during our exchange.

"This is incredible! I too must come to Machu Picchu. I do not want to miss such a special event," he announces.

"Yes, of course. Come along too, Alberto. It will be great to have you join us," Eliceu replies as I nod in agreement.

"All right then, I'll clear my schedule and make my reservations," Alberto says, beaming with enthusiasm.

The stage is now set for a profound sequence of events. The mysterious forces contained within the *Light of the Masters* would soon shine forth and illuminate the way.

With a gust of putrid, smoggy air, a dozen Peruvian cab drivers hover around us in the main hall of the Lima terminal.

"Taxi, sirs?"

"¿*Taxi, señors?* Hey guys, need a taxi?"

"*No, gracias.* No. *No, gracias.* No!" I snap back.

Clearly these guys are the paparazzi of the ground transportation community. They just won't take no for an answer. Alberto steps in and quickly dispels them with a simple hand movement. He merely wags his index finger back and forth, and they disperse like wayward fruit flies.

"What was that, Alberto? Some kind of secret South American finger code?"

In response he gives me a simple nonjudgmental grin and a subtle nodding of his head. That's one of the things I like about Alberto, he never jabs or tries to prove anything. If there is a lesson to be learned, such as the ways of a culture, he won't try to push it. This humble approach makes it easy for me to see into myself and make the changes I feel would benefit me most. As we make our way to the Aero Continente ticket counter for our connecting flight to Cusco, I wag my finger back and forth practicing. I'm not sure whether or not I'm mastering it, but the quizzical "What is this gringo doing?" reaction I get from the local travelers tells me I'm certainly making an impression.

Alberto leads the way to the ticket counter and checks us in. Within an hour we are boarding an aging jetliner. I say "aging" because of the dents on the fuselage, the fluids leaking from under the belly of the engines and the black soot stains on its tail section.

The roar of the engines triggers widened eyes as we bounce our way down Lima's dilapidated runway. With surprising ease, the jet gently lifts off and begins its steep climb. Looking out the left side window, I see shadows cast by the plane eclipse an unending array of poverty-stricken structures. The thick Lima fog quickly obscures my field of vision as beads of condensation streak across my weathered and cracked window portal. In a moment of clearing, the foothills of Lima slowly transform into lush green granite peaks thrusting up into the sky like massive terrestrial teeth.

Climbing to an altitude of twelve thousand feet, we fly without incident over the Andes for almost an hour. Suddenly, we make a sharp sixty-degree left turn as the jet soars between two close-knit mountain ranges. Sheer rock cliffs loom on all sides as the golden Peruvian sun reflects off their smooth granite faces. Like a celestial flying key, our plane makes its way through the lock of crags and into the awesome highlands of the Andes. Distant ridges of stone shimmer with snow-capped peaks as steel colored clouds hover gently around them. Just a few miles ahead lay Cusco, the last big city prior to reaching Machu Picchu. Straining my neck to look out the window I spot a multitude of red ceramic tile roofs glowing in the sun. Between the buildings I see a myriad of dirt roadways circumventing clusters of adobe buildings. A group of silver water towers glistens and reflects rays of light back into my widened eyes. Filling the entire valley are lush green patches of land interspersed with rocky crags and granite peaks. The Andes descend into the valley, stretching their massive stone toes far into the fertile fields.

Just ahead I spot a small black asphalt runway and watch in anticipation as we make our final approach. Within moments, a slamming blast reverberates up from the belly of the plane. I look around for a reality check, but no one seems to care about the incident. Even the chicken sitting on the lap of an aging laborer seems unaffected. Veering wildly to the left and right, we slow to taxi speed as the Spanish-speaking flight attendant calmly welcomes us to Cusco.

Cusco is South America's oldest continuously inhabited city and has a population of just over three hundred thousand people. Built consistent with the Inca philosophy of dividing agricultural and urban sectors, the Sapi River evenly bisects the city. Ancient rock walls with the mysterious razor-sharp cuts are integrated into the foundations of the buildings in both the new and old parts of town. Cusco thrived even before Columbus arrived in the Americas, and later became the center of the Western Hemisphere's greatest empire. Legend has it that Cusco was founded in the twelfth century by Manco Capac, the "Son of the Sun," one of eight ancient Gods and the first Inca king. Arriving at the fertile valley, he pierced the earth with a magical golden staff marking Cusco as the birthplace of the Inca civilization. Today the place is called *el qosqo*, or the "earth's navel" by the Incas.

As I climb down the jet's skinny steps, the first things I see in every direction are gigantic mountain peaks jutting up to the sky. Tracing the descending ridges downward they all merge into the gentle valley of Cusco. It looks to me as if this place is being held in divine hands. The air is extremely thin and dry. My eyes water from the lack of moisture and my lungs revolt, asking for more air to breathe. Going from almost sea level to twelve thousand feet within an hour is a real shock to the system. Step by step I make my way down the jet's metal staircase. I glance over at the left engine. Black fluid drips from its underside, gathering in a massive puddle on the tarmac. Part of me is relieved and part is unsettled, knowing that I will probably be boarding this old bird again in a few days for my return trip.

In the tiny terminal, Alberto and I are greeted by a huge, eight-foot-tall, bronze Inca wall mask. Its gold and green colors illuminate an expressionless face as it hauntingly directs us toward the threshold of eternity . . . and to the baggage claim area. The terminal at Cusco has a completely different feel from that of Lima. The people are laid back and very easygoing. It feels like a small farm town back in the States where country folk slowly saunter down their lazy little streets. With an air of excitement, Alberto and I collect our backpacks and head for the front of the terminal. Just above the exit doors are five massive surrealistic murals painted in crimson and greens and blacks, depicting ancient Inca Gods bestowing their powers upon the earth—a fitting display for what is about to occur for us.

"*¿Taxi, amigos?*"

"*¡Sí, Cusco por favor!*" Alberto replies quickly.

In a split second a young man snatches our gear and loads it into the trunk of his cab. As we jump in, Alberto rattles off the name of our hotel in Spanish and the car takes off like a rocket. As my head jerks back and hits the rear seat pad I think, cab drivers from around the world must go to the same driving school—the one that teaches them to be mobile chiropractors. As we head for town I decide to experiment with my Spanish, so I strike up a conversation with our driver.

"*¿Nombre, por favor?*" I ask.

"*¡Julio!*" he immediately replies smiling broadly into the rearview mirror. His skimpy mustache and dark skin complement his big pearly white teeth.

"*Mi nombre, Val Jon,*" I say.

"*¿Wall Juan?*" he asks, struggling with the pronunciation while wildly veering around a vegetable cart on the right side of the road.

"*¡Sí! Juan Valdez,*" I quickly reply to save him any embarrassment and to save my life.

"*¡Ahh! Juan Valdez,*" he fires back, grinning again into the rearview mirror.

Through more artful dialogue, Alberto tells me that Julio is of Inca decent and has spent his entire life in Cusco. Married with two small children, he had just recently purchased his cab and was saving his money to buy a house just outside of town for his family. Upon Julio's emphatic and cheerful recommendation, we opt for a short tour of the city to get acquainted with Cusco, and to help fund his new home.

As our friendly host drives us through the city, we pass open markets and groups of native people. Tradition and history are etched in their faces, and their colorful attire hints of their playful communal spirits. The ladies wear multicolored shawls, long multilayered skirts and tattered, wide-brimmed farmer hats. Merchant booths are stuffed with vegetables, car parts and cheap jewelry. Trinket stands and vegetable bins litter the sidewalks as bright blue roof tarps flap gently in the breeze. When I roll down the window to get a better look, strange combinations of smells attack my nose. Odors of fresh fish, pungent herbs and motor oil flood into the cab causing me to immediately reverse the direction of the window handle.

Traveling deeper into the heart of the city, we come upon a huge public square called the Plaza de Armas. In the central square is a massive, circular stone-carved water fountain flowing with sparkling water. The plaza is skirted by colonial arcades filled with gift shops, restaurants, pubs and curio shops. Native street vendors and young shoeshine boys line the sidewalks and roam the plaza. On the northeastern side of the square an ancient Inca cathedral is flanked by the churches of Jesus Maria and El Trinunfo, while the double-steepled church of La Compania graces the southeastern side. In the western corner of the plaza, portions of the original foundation walls from the Inca Palace of Pachacutec still stand.

Julio drives us away from the square, up Sol Avenue, and then lets us out to see one of Cusco's most popular sites, the Temple of the Sun, now enshrined within a huge Catholic Church. The ancient site is shrouded in mysterious, otherworldly lore. The clusters of temple rooms within the walls of the church were used by the Inca to worship the sun, moon and the stars. The precision of the stonework is remarkable and the astronomical and solar orientations are astounding. It has been speculated by some Westerners that the temple's open stone doorways may be of extraterrestrial origin and thus used as "gateways" into other dimensions, similar to a wormhole in space. Step into the doorway here and you may well step out somewhere far away. An interesting point is that more than one hundred miles away there is a "sister" Sun Temple within the ruins of Machu Picchu. Who knows, perhaps they were used in unison as a kind of "metaphysical transporter."

I enter the church and wind my way around to one of the temples. The structure is about eight feet tall and has a rectangular portal at its center that leads nowhere but to the heavens. Moving closer, I definitely get an otherworldly feel from it. I slowly step through the eerie stone doorway. For a brief moment I become disoriented and have to lean against its vertical stone wall to regain my sense of balance. It could be the altitude that caused my moment of weakness, but whatever the cause, it takes a few moments to regain my faculties. As I back out of the opening, I suddenly see a fleeting image of what looks like the feathered wing of a black bird.

"Are you all right, Val Jon?" Alberto asks.

"Yes. I'm all right, but something very strange just happened."

"What was it? What did you experience?"

"I was fine until I stepped through the opening."

"By the look on your face, it was as if you saw something or had some kind of insight," he probes further.

"Now that you mention it, there *was* something. Just for a moment I caught a glimpse of what looked like . . . a flying black bird."

There's something spooky about this encounter. Alberto and I jointly decide to call it a day and get to our hotel. Exiting the church, we return to our cab and ask Julio to drive us to the Libertador Hotel. The Libertador is one of Cusco's finest hotels. In addition to being modern and luxurious, its foundation and walls are remnants of the ancient palace of Francisco Pizarro, conqueror and first Governor of Peru. The huge 214-room hotel showcases a six-foot-high perimeter wall of classic Inca stonework. Inside the granite walls, plush antique furniture and fantastic Inca art create a rich ambiance fit for royalty. Over a light dinner and cocoa leaf tea, Alberto and I joke about being of royal blood and joyfully plan our pilgrimage to Machu Picchu.

The following morning, Julio picks us up in front of the hotel and delivers us to the Santa Ana train station in downtown Cusco. As we step out of the cab, he passes us our backpacks and we say our good-byes. Alberto fires off a few Spanish gestures, places some soles, the Peruvian currency, in Julio's hand and pats him gently on the shoulder. Anticipation fills the moment as we sprint up the ancient stone steps and into the train station. Again, Alberto handles all the logistical arrangements, and leads the way to the correct boarding area. What a thrill to step up into the antiquated Pullman class boxcar. Its yellow and burnt orange colors, coupled with the old-fashioned vertical slider windows bring smiles to our faces. Inside the air is cool and carries a scent of old leather and diesel soot. All the windows are open in the boxcar and the early morning chill runs through my body. Alberto pats me on the back warmly and points to our assigned seats.

A blast from the train whistle marks the beginning of our slow ascent into the agricultural highlands of the Andes. Soot from the diesel engine engulfs the boxcar, temporarily clouding our view of the city. Through the thick black smoke we catch a glimpse of Cusco out the left side of the train. The cathedral in the Plaza de Armas stands tall and proud in the dawn's early glow as lights on its steeple twinkle brightly. As we gain altitude on the railway, both the agricultural sector and the urban sectors of the city come slowly into view.

In addition to the view of the city out the left side of the train, the right side yields a close-up view of the hillside ghetto dwellings. As we roll past poverty-stricken areas, I peer into a multitude of dirt-floored shacks containing cardboard boxes for tables and dust-covered jars for food storage. The golden morning sun illuminates the streams of open sewage that run down steep red and brown clay ravines. Scores of children wearing colorful ragged clothing mingle with pigs and wild dogs as they snoop through trash and debris for smatterings of food. Gleaming, black innocent eyes peer out from small, dirty, weathered faces, evoking an uneasy feeling within me.

As I look upon the squalor, my eyes come upon a little Peruvian girl. Examining her more closely I notice she has long, straight black hair and an innocent, tender face. She's wearing a brightly colored woven sweater with no pants, revealing her tiny bare bottom. She has nothing—little food, inadequate shelter and no future to speak of, but she smiles and eagerly waves at the train as it blows its hollow whistle three times. Seeing her enthusiasm makes me feel better about her condition, but I can't help feeling compassion and empathy for her.

Good morning, little Inca beauty, I whisper, as my heart swells and tears flow down my humble face.

CHAPTER FOUR

ETERNALITY:

THE SECOND DIMENSION OF KNOWING

Everlasting nothing, so divine are your eyes
Temporal delights fill eternal minds
Feet of gold and heart of fire!
To the center of your being soars my soul's desire
Holding my life in the grace of your heart
Illusions of karma dance in the darkness
As I reach for your sweetness
I find you right here
Everlasting nothing beside me so near

In the ruins far below, the ceremonial flames flicker with melodic cadence. It looks as if the people holding the torches are swaying in a unified, blissful dance. Out of the corner of my eye, to the left of the Seat of the Condor, I spot another dancing image—shadows from another flame. Again, visions of the *Inca Fire* blaze with its yellow and red ribbons of light. The flames, I sense immediately, are a precursor for another journey into my past. What memories will be illuminated this time? And what lessons will they bring? As the next mysterious message comes forth, I write it down, word for word.

29

The Light of the Masters reveals the second dimension, Eternality.
The notion of mastery, in light of the truth, can only be known
through the resilience of the soul and open embrace of open embrace.

The *Inca Fire* draws me into its center and into another dimension, another time and place. Memories of the previous year and of my travels to India come streaming into my consciousness— memories that will soon lead me into the infinite realm of *Eternality.*

The roar of a million motor scooters screams through my head, snarling and tangling the traffic of my thought. Grotesque, ancient, armor-clad figures, illuminated by searing flames of crimson and orange, dance around my pounding temples. Sweat streams from my pores, cementing me to the thin muslin sheets that cover my shivering body. When I open my eyes, the blur of unfamiliar Indian décor adds to my disorientation and sickness.

"What is happening to me!" I blurt out.

Reverberations of slurred words merge with the twisted sounds within my pounding skull. Reaching for the low table next to the bed, my swollen hand sends the telephone careening across the polished wooden floor. Leaning off the right side of the bed, I fall to my knees and crawl toward the direction of the pulsing tone. Each labored move thrusts me to the edge of convulsions as a fever rages inside my body. I pull the phone to me, punch the "0" button and soon hear the soothing voice of my hotel contact, Eric. Two weeks earlier, Eric had picked me up at the airport and transported me to the Taj West End Hotel, in Bangalore, India. A young man in his mid thirties, Eric is both kind and professional. Like most people from his culture, his hair is jet-black and his body thin. He walks with a spring in his step and always has a smile on his face. We had come to know each other through discussing the history and culture of India and America, and sharing personal insights about spirituality, art and literature.

My visit to India resulted from a combination of business and personal desire. In summer 1997 I had been brought there by an international firm to provide their people leadership development training. In addition to my work, I wanted to learn about the culture and see some of India's ancient spiritual shrines. Little did I know I would soon be visiting a present day shrine blessed with one of India's most revered spiritual masters, Sai Baba.

"Mr. Farris? Are you all right? You sound very bad, very bad indeed."

"Eric, I've got a fever and I feel very sick. Would you call a doctor for me?"

"Yes, of course Mr. Farris. I'll take care of it directly. Try to relax in the meantime."

"All right Eric. Thank you very much."

As I hang up the phone I think that if I can make it to the bathroom, perhaps I can splash cold water over my body and bring the fever down. I struggle to my feet but before I can put weight on my legs they fold underneath me, causing me to fall to my knees. Holding myself steady for a moment, I close my eyes, and as I do, an image comes rushing into my mind. It's a vision of an Indian woman clad in an orange loincloth, kneeling before a beautiful golden altar. She appears to be deep in prayer, her hands are pressed together, resting on her dark-skinned forehead. The image then disappears and I turn to fall back into the sweat-soaked bed. As I roll onto my back, the heat forces me into a gut-wrenching moan. Then I have a flash of insight:

My sickness has something to do with my visit with Sai Baba. I'm sure of it. Sai Baba, known also as "Swami," is one of the most influential spiritual leaders in all of India. Millions of people from all walks of life believe he is the world's current day Avatar. An Avatar is a divine entity manifest in human form, much like Christ. The word "Avatar" in Sanskrit means "entity of divine incarnation." The God Shiva in ancient Hinduism was one such entity. An Avatar is a direct manifestation of God in physical form, whose role is to be the source of spiritual well-being for all races. Avatars are said to appear during times of planetary strife or when spiritual rejuvenation is needed. Like a sun's gravity attracts and holds its revolving planets in orbit, an Avatar attracts and holds those who are on a spiritual path. As individuals "orbit " around the Avatar, they receive warmth, love, spiritual encouragement and blessings.

Avatar or not, unlike many spiritual leaders, Sai Baba does not promote secular doctrine. Rather, he promotes that all religions and faiths of the world are holy. He believes that any means of worship and devotion contributes to the betterment of humanity. His philosophy is very simple—love all and serve all. His messages about unconditional love and humanitarianism are carried to every corner of the earth. In terms of daily discipline and spiritual philosophy, Sai Baba often refers to the ancient texts of the Vedas, which embodies two kinds of Dharma, or codes of conduct, called "Nivrithi" and "Pravrithi." Nivrithi is the inward path, which teaches knowledge of the higher Self, the inner spirit and the ways of consciousness. Pravrithi is the outward path, which teaches about the qualities and values needed for living in the day-to-day world. It is the inclusion of both the inner world and the outer world that Sai Baba demonstrates and teaches his disciples. Sai Baba speaks about his mission here on earth in this way:

> My mission is to raise the consciousness of man to the level at which he neither rejoices nor mourns over anything. In that supreme state, one is going through rebirth and redeath each moment, for these acts are one and the same, emerging from the formless into form, merging from the form into the formless. Then, there is no success or adversity, no joy or pain. When the devotee attains this oneness, his journey towards me ceases. For, he will be with me endlessly.

My illness started just one day after being with Sai Baba at his ashram, Prashaanthi Nilayam, located in the southern region of India. During my stay I attended a number of darshans with two Indian friends who had arranged the trip. A "darshan" is a formal event in which Sai Baba walks among his visitors and devotees, being with them and blessing them. My hosts for the trip were father and daughter—Narayan and Sai. Narayan, a gentle soul in his late fifties, is a longtime devotee of Swami whom I met through his daughter "Sai." Sai, named after the master himself, is a spirited young woman who works at the company I had been contracted to consult with. Because my leadership program contained elements of humanity and spirituality, I think she felt comfortable in asking me if I would like to meet her father and possibly visit Sai Baba.

Narayan and Sai knew all the logistical details of journeying to Swami's ashram. They made the arrangements, including transportation, entrance into the ashram and accommodations. During our six-hour cab ride to Prashaanthi Nilayam, they told me countless stories of miracles they had witnessed Sai Baba perform over the years. Narayan himself had even been healed. He recounted an event ten years earlier, in which he was walking across a busy street when a passing motor scooter caught him by the pant leg and dragged him fifty feet down the roadway. The accident resulted in a badly mangled left leg, broken in six places. X-rays revealed terrible news—the only feasible option was to amputate his leg. Distraught, Narayan decided to visit Sai Baba and ask for a healing. Swami immediately recognized him out of the crowd, walked up to him, touched his hip and said, "Don't worry about your injury. It will be gone by tomorrow, midday." Three days later a second set of x-rays revealed that his bones were completely healed! I sat stunned in the back seat of the cab as he pulled up his pant leg and showed me the grotesque external scarring that remained.

The darshan hall inside Sai Baba's ashram holds well over fifty thousand people. On most days, between eight and twenty thousand people attend darshan. When empty, the hall's black marble floor shines with buffed perfection. The evenly spaced ceiling pillars distributed in the open air auditorium sparkle with images of ancient gods, reeds and flowers. The ceiling is adorned with over a thousand six-foot-square honeycombed recesses, each containing a beautiful golden lotus blossom. The massive, one-hundred-foot-long stage is decorated with two lifesized carved stone lions and a vast array of colorful fresh flower arrangements. When filled, the hall is divided into three parts: in the center and up front near the stage sit Sai Baba's closest disciples, servants and the students that attend his university just outside the ashram. The right side of the hall is reserved for women and the left side for men. Segregation of the sexes is part of religious doctrine in India. At the beginning of darshan, Sai Baba always enters from the right and travels through a pathway of six-foot-wide aisles, designated with inlaid white marble, that wind through the hall. As he travels through the intricate human labyrinth, he bestows blessings, passes out holy ash and collects letters from his devotees.

At darshan one morning, Narayan and I were fortunate enough to be in the front row of an aisle, so we knew Sai Baba would pass close to us at some point. The program for darshan is to engage in prayer, bhajan or spiritual songs, and then blessings from Swami. The whole event takes an hour and a half. Every aspect of darshan is inspiring. On this particular morning, more than eight thousand people sang together about kindness, love and compassion. Waves of inspiration swept through me each time the group leader sang solo and then everyone in the hall repeated the words in melodic unison.

Shortly after bhajan, Sai Baba entered the hall. All eight thousand people knelt down in unison and clasped their hands together in prayer. A thunderous silence fell over the crowd. Peering to the far end of the auditorium I spotted him. He was a small-framed man, no more than five-feet tall. His body seemed frail, yet he moved with the grace of a swan. He wore a simple orange robe that draped down and covered his feet. His biggest distinguishing feature was his huge, black afro-style hairdo.

Like a human wave, clusters of people gently rose up and swayed toward him offering gifts, notes and letters as he passed. Occasionally, but infrequently, he stopped to accept their letters and bless them with vibhuti. (Vibhuti is a holy ash that Sai Baba manifests from his hands. Resembling the ash created through cremation, it has a sweet divine fragrance similar to sandalwood incense. According to Indian theologians, vibhuti is composed of ethereal particles that Swami gathers from the ends of the universe and brings together in the form of a sacred ash. It symbolizes the paradox between the illusion of mortality and the eternal nature of the soul.)

The hall felt electric as he glided through the masses bestowing his blessings. Sitting up straight, I watched his every move. Time after time he moved his hand in a circular motion creating vibhuti right out of thin air. If I hadn't seen it with my own eyes I wouldn't have believed it. It was no trick though. His sleeves hung just below his elbows exposing his dark thin forearms, so there was no way he could sleight of hand what I witnessed. Ten or more times I watched him manifest mounds of the gray ash in his open palm. At one point he stopped in front of an old man holding a small ornate chest the size of a shoe box. As the man raised the box toward him, Sai Baba rotated his right hand. As he did, a bluish white flash of light appeared in his palm and then, without blinking an eye, I witnessed a two-inch-high mound of vibhuti appear in his open palm! He then turned his hand downward and the ash began pouring into the box until it flowed out over the edges. Fine dust filled the air in every direction as people bowed down in reverence and awe.

Sai Baba moved closer to Narayan and me until he was less than twenty feet away. I kept my eyes on his face and hoped he would make eye contact with me. The moment after I had that thought, he looked right into me. His deep eyes were like whirlpools swirling into an ocean of eternity. His presence was like no other human being I have ever met. There was a profound sense of grandeur about him and he projected a paradoxical persona. He possessed the features and characteristics of a child, innocent and pure, and yet he also exuded an ancient wisdom and timeless grace. Although our eye contact lasted only a split second, I got a glimpse into the vastness of eternity. Time stopped. Everything within my reality fell away into a nondescript void, like looking into two mirrors facing each other and being drawn down the curved reflections into infinity.

Sai Baba then walked directly toward Narayan and me and stopped right in front of us. What an incredible moment! I was stunned, but Narayan knew exactly what to do. Sai Baba waited there until Narayan pulled back the hem of his robe so we could touch his feet. Taking the cue, I quickly reached down and placed my hand on the tops of Swami's feet. What an incredible surprise it was! Although he was over seventy years old, his feet were as soft and supple as the skin of a newborn baby. As I touched him gently, I asked for his blessing in my life and to be with me throughout my journeys. The response was instantaneous. It would be so. I then felt a tingling sensation similar to a light electrical shock traveling up my arm and into the center of my chest. I didn't know it at the time, but this transfer of energy would have profound implications for me. Sai Baba then moved on down the aisle and left the hall through a side door near the stage.

After darshan that morning, Narayan informed me that we had just been blessed in a most remarkable way. He enthusiastically explained that in all his years of being with Swami and seeing him greet hundreds of thousands of visitors, he rarely let anyone physically touch him. For him to stop in front of us and allow us to do so was a profound occurrence. It was certainly an event I would never forget.

The fever raging inside me is unforgettable as well. Vivid flashes of color and splintered mosaic images flutter under my sweat soaked eyelids. When I open my eyes, grotesque hallucinations taunt my sanity. The walls move and the ceiling sinks down around me. Sounds magnify as I strain to sort out the distorted blur of input. Then I hear what sounds like a thumping at the door. I have trouble telling if it's real or not, but when Eric walks into my room, my confusion clears.

"Here is the doctor you asked for, Val Jon. He will take care of you," Eric says in a concerned tone.

After a short greeting, the doctor pulls a stethoscope and

thermometer from his tattered black leather bag. The cold metal disk he presses against my body causes a shock wave of chills, pushing me to the edge of convulsions. Fortunately, the thermometer in my mouth allows me to close my lips tightly around it, so as to avert vomiting.

"You have no internal damage that I can detect," he says softly in broken English. "However, you do have a temperature above 103 degrees. I want to give you an injection to bring the fever down."

"Doctor, please, I don't want an injection," I plead.

"You are in a dangerous state and if your fever does not come down it could cause damage to your vital organs," he replies sternly.

"This may sound strange, but I was with Sai Baba yesterday. Do you know him?" I ask.

"Yes, of course. Everyone in India knows of Sai Baba," he replies softly.

"During darshan, he let me touch his feet and soon after that I started feeling ill. I believe it has something to do with my fever, so I feel I must deal with this thing naturally. Can you understand?" I ask.

"Yes, I understand. Many people report such symptoms after being with Sai Baba. In this case I will give you some oral medication instead, but you must take it every four hours and check in with me first thing tomorrow. If you do this I will be satisfied."

"Yes. I will follow your directions. Thank you," I reply gratefully.

He then hands me two packets of medication and we say our good-byes. After he leaves, my sight is still blurry and I have trouble breathing. Lying back on the bed, the image of the loin-clothed devotee returns to me. She bows in reverence before the golden altar again. This time I make a connection that she is one of Sai Baba's devotees and is here to give me a message. The message has to do with surrendering myself to Swami's teachings, which includes giving up all my worldly vices and desires. This message is rather bad news for me. You see, I like my vices. I know it's not the "spiritual" thing to say, but it's true. I plan on giving them up just before I die so I can have a good time until the last possible moment. Apparently this plan is frowned upon, because my fever is getting much worse, forcing me to the verge of passing out.

Wiping the sweat from my brow, I notice it's almost eight o'clock. I suddenly remember that Narayan is going to meet me for dinner in the hotel restaurant at eight p.m. I'm in no shape to dine, but I know it's very important to see him, especially considering what is happening to me. I pick up the phone again and call Eric.

"Hello? Eric? This is Val Jon. What? Yes, I'm feeling about the same, but the doctor gave me some medication that I'm sure will help. Yes, I'll call you if I need anything. I have a favor to ask. Please send my dinner guest Narayan to my room when he arrives at the restaurant. He will be there soon and will be asking for me. So you'll recognize him, he's in his late fifties, has a thin mustache and walks with a slight limp. Good. Thank you. Yes, I will. Good-bye."

Ten minutes later Narayan walks through the door of my hotel room. When he sees my condition, he quickly moves to the left side of my bed.

"Val Jon, what is happening to you? You do not look well."

"Narayan, I have come down with a bad fever and I'm very sick."

"When did this begin?" he asks.

"I started feeling weak right after we returned from Sai Baba's ashram."

"I know exactly what is happening to you. It is Samscar from Swami!"

"Samscar? What is Samscar?" I ask.

"I have seen this many times. Of those lucky few who ever get to touch Swami, many of them become deathly ill with fever. It's a special and wonderful thing because it begins the process of surrendering to the Avatar," he answers with a wide timeless smile.

"This 'special and wonderful thing' is about to kill me, Narayan. I am burning up inside!"

"Do not worry Val Jon, it will only kill what must die within you for you to join Sai Baba in his mission here on Earth."

"Oh, goodie," I reply meekly as I close my eyes in misery.

Narayan explains that Samscar is a kind of "repair shop" for the soul. The repairs are done on a spiritual level and are said to prepare people to "orbit" closer to the Avatar. Although a little "woo-woo" sounding to me, it makes sense at one level. If an Avatar is hot like the sun, those moving closer to him had better be able to cope with the heat.

"I'll be back in just a moment. I'm going to bring something that will help you," he says as he heads for the door. In a few minutes he returns with a brown paper sack. Moving this time to the right side of my bed, he kneels down close to me.

"Val Jon, I brought some of Sai Baba's vibhuti for you. Let me put it on your chest. If you ask Swami to help you, he will take your fever away within minutes," he says, as he pours out the gray ash from small white plastic packets.

As Narayan rubs the vibhuti onto my chest and neck I become mesmerized by its intoxicatingly sweet smell. In addition to its sweetness, its scent evokes a strange sense of what I can only describe as an "ancient familiarity." The first thing I notice is that the vibhuti has an immediate calming effect on me. My body relaxes and I feel a gentle euphoria throughout my system, but there is something else. I also experience a profound feeling of connectedness. I can't tell exactly what I feel connected to, but it's similar to being included in a large gathering of people who know me and care deeply for me.

The vibhuti's powerful effects stun me. In twenty minutes my fever has completely vanished! Before I know it I'm sitting up in bed laughing and talking with Narayan as if nothing had ever happened.

"You see, Val Jon. Swami will answer all your prayers. All you must do is ask."

"Yes. I see that, Narayan. I also want to thank you for coming tonight and for bringing the vibhuti to me."

"You need not thank me. Instead, thank Swami for his eternal grace and love. That is all that is required."

"Yes. I do thank him. I am very grateful. Very grateful indeed."

As I lie here next to my friend Narayan I feel blessed. I reflect on being with Sai Baba and especially on the moment he allowed me to touch him. The energy that ran up my arm and into my chest not only triggered a fever, it opened my heart as well.

In the months after returning from India I noticed a number of shifts in my life. The first was an increased ability to feel compassion for others. It's as if my heart has gained the wisdom to allow people to be just as they are, without needing to change them in any way. Additionally, there is a sense of trust in my life that I never fully had before. I no longer fear death in any way. A part of me now knows that death is an illusion and my soul is immortal, eternal and totally indestructible. I also experience a greater sense of endurance and an ability to stay engaged in the difficult challenges that life brings me. I feel as if Sai Baba is always here, right next to me, every day of my life.

A gentle, ancient calm delivers me back to the Seat of the Condor. Looking out over the distant landscape of the Andes, I feel whole and connected, like I belong here. I'm no longer just a visitor, a spectator or even an explorer:

> I'm now a part of this place. I'm an expression of its past, its present and its distant future. I'm its brother and sister, its son and mother. I am its rock and its sky and even its inspiration on high. I am also its valleys and caves, its darkness and night and surely its shadowy nature that creeps across the light. I am a part of its infinite movement and its eternal stillness, and I shall gladly move with it and embrace its sacred will.

Now I am aware of *two* Dimensions of Knowing—*Humility* and *Eternality*. In addition to having a degree of humility, my reflections about being with Sai Baba provide me with a vivid reminder that part of me is eternal and indestructible. It's the part of the human spirit that refuses to give up, even in the face of total annihilation; drives us to rebuild if our homes are demolished due to natural disasters; demands our greatness and inspires us to endure all the hardships in the world in order to keep providing for ourselves and for our children. It's the part of us that values life and holds sacred everything in the world.

Humility and *Eternality*, I realize, work together in a powerful way. Not only am I gaining the ability to be more open and more resilient, I'm seeing a third, more powerful result. Because *Eternality* illuminates the indestructibility of my soul, I now see that I will have more patience, more compassion and a much longer "fuse" in my relationships in the future. This *burn zone* becomes more fascinating to me with each memory and insight. I no longer fear the *Inca Fire*. I am now willing to fully surrender myself to it and like my friend Narayan said, let it burn away the limitations and constraints within me that keep me from accessing more powerful aspects of myself.

The double steepled church of La Compania graces the Plaza De Armas in downtown Cusco.

CHAPTER FIVE

FROM CUSCO TO AGUAS CALIENTES

How in the world does a soul see?
Through a distant ancient lens
untouched by hands mortal or nay
Aged, old and bent by the cyclical breath
of master upon master
Crystal clear, sharpened by vast
and frozen eons of forever
On the winds of the past, the future
and the everlasting now
This is how in the world a soul does see

As the train rolls past the bare-bottomed little Inca girl, her innocence and tenderness humble me deeply as I wave good-bye to her. There is a richness and wisdom about the Inca people that transcends their physical poverty. They possess a strength that enables them to endure incredible hardships and still retain a true sense of joy and peace. I am learning much on this expedition and I am grateful.

Looking ahead, I notice we're traveling into the agricultural highlands of the Andes. This fertile farming plateau supplies hundreds of varieties of beans and potatoes to neighboring towns. Rich green and golden fields woven together into a magical tapestry of abundance fill my awestruck eyes. A maze of dirt pathways and clusters of old and crumbling Inca dwellings are scattered throughout the landscape. The well placed stones still hold the shapes cast by their builders. Images come to mind of natives living in the huts, working the land and worshipping the natural world around them. I imagine whole generations of Inca farmers sharing their lives, living off the land, making a life with only what nature provided and what their devoted hands could yield.

Then, as if by magic, my musings spring to life. There, coming into view just ahead is an Inca family living in one of the historic relics. What a sight to behold. As the train approaches, chickens scatter in every direction and a group of small children jump up and down with excitement. Behind the children, two women in white-brimmed top hats wash clothes on the river rocks, and just to their left, three men in ragged pants work the fields. All at once, the entire family rises up and greets the slow-moving train. They all smile and wave joyously. I impulsively raise my camera to get a shot, but lower it in respect when I realize I need not capture the image on film as it will be indelibly imprinted in my heart. Never in all my travels have I come across people who greeted me with such dignity and respect. Here I am in their world, with more material possessions than they will ever have, enjoying the splendor of their land without having to pay the price of enduring their hardship, and still, they welcome me with such warmth. It gives new meaning to the word hospitality.

Continuing on the rickety railroad tracks, I watch as the highlands slowly transform into the Sacred Valley of the Incas. The descent from the highlands at about 12,000 feet, to the valley floor at less than 1,000 feet above sea level, is a major drop. The train tracks precariously zigzag their way down into the gorge until we are right in the heart of the Sacred Valley and at eye level with the Urubamba River. It is called the "Sacred Valley" because of the temperate climate, rich soil, "celestial" river and majestic mountains that embrace it on all sides. Additionally, the terrain along the valley floor has great spiritual and cosmological relevance for the

Inca people. The entire valley, from the town of Pisaq all the way to the ruins at Machu Picchu, has been modeled after the cosmos. The Urubamba River, often called the "Mayu," or "Celestial River," is said to mirror the Milky Way. Many of the constellations, including Orion, Scorpio and the Southern Cross are charted in rock formations and hand-carved ritual sites along the banks of the river.

Still today, many people living in the rural communities believe that the forces that exist beyond the earth, such as God, the Sun, the Moon and the Stars have limited power until they are represented on the earth as landmarks. Once the landmarks are correlated with the divine forces, they become incarnate and thus control man's destiny. Speaking with our Peruvian boxcar attendant I learn that there are seven such landmarks in the Sacred Valley. The first is the constellation of the Condor, which is located in Pisaq, thirty-two kilometers from Cusco. The "Cuntur Orcco," or Condor's Peak, is a ritual site composed of terraces carved into the hillside in the shape of a huge bird. The Condor, as I mentioned earlier, represents the Being nearest to the Divine and is said to be the intermediary charged with carrying the spirits or life forces of the Inca people to the eternal resting place of their ancestors.

The second landmark, the Tree of Origins, or "Mallqui," is a huge agricultural development in the town of Ollantaytambo built in the shape of an upside-down tree. The term "Mallqui" represents not only a living tree, but also a symbolic genealogical tree for the dead. Just as there are family trees for the living, this site provides protection and belonging for the souls that have passed on from this world.

The third site, also near the town of Ollantaytambo, is called "Catachillay," or the Astral Llama. This site is modeled after a star constellation just below the Southern Cross, which includes Alpha and Beta Centauri. Again terraces are carved out of the side of a mountain, depicting the shape of a female llama lying next to her young offspring. The symbolism is that the llama drinks from the great river of the Milky Way and brings its mystical and immense power down to the earth in the form of rain and river water. Astronomically, the site was used to determine the best time for breeding livestock and planting.

The fourth landmark, "Tanpuquiro," or The Corn City, located in the ancient urban section of Ollantaytambo, is still inhabited to this day. This section of the city was modeled after an ear of corn, and its structures were built like rows of teeth or corn on a cob. The site is associated with Mother Corn, who is the ancient mother of productivity or the essential spirit which first gave life to corn. Corn represents more than food for the Inca people. It is also made into a drink called "ajha" or "chicha," which is used during important spiritual rituals and magical practices.

The fifth site is "Inticcahuarina," or The Astronomical Observation Area near Ollantaytambo. A remarkable stone-carved sundial called "Pachaunanchango," or "the knower of time," was used by astrologers, wise men and priests to determine the cycles of nature and the changing of seasons. Using a series of notches in the rock coupled with shadows cast by stone protrusions, they were able to pinpoint exact dates and times for both summer and winter solstices.

The sixth landmark is the "Huaca of Chinpaccahua," or Man Who Looks Ahead. Legend tells that long ago the sky turned black and all the plants, flowers and fruits of the earth disappeared. Then a wise man consulted the Condor, who was old and wise, and asked for a way to bring back the sun. The answer was to throw all the remaining food into the lake and have faith in the Gods. Following this commandment, the man did as he was told and the next day, miraculously, the sun came back into the world and all the vegetation returned. He was subsequently honored by all the Inca people, and his face was immortalized on a high cliff called "Pankuylluna." Today the face can be seen carved into the mountainside outside of Ollantaytambo. On the day of the winter solstice, June 21, the face is perfectly illuminated by the rays of the sun.

The seventh site is my destination, Machu Picchu, which lies at the far end of the Sacred Valley. This beautiful stone sanctuary is the crown jewel in the cosmological landscape of Inca philosophy. It is in that place above the clouds, that all the magical and mysterious forces of the earth and sky coalesce. The site was modeled after the mythical Peruvian Condor and, according to legend, when mankind sinks into spiritual disorder the Sun sends his messenger "Llulli" to restore order in the world. Llulli is described as a huge bird, even larger than a Condor, with brilliant iridescent wings, whose presence evokes reverence and peace for all who behold it. The souls of people are thus transported to the essential nature of truth, which lies beyond time and within the heart of God.

"Aguas Calientes is the next stop," Alberto nudges me gently.

"What an incredibly beautiful culture this is, Alberto. Seeing these families really brings the Inca civilization to life for me. Right here, living in these huts along the river, are the ancestral souls of those who built Machu Picchu."

"Indeed you are right. Seeing how these people live is a big part of understanding the *Light of the Masters*, I just know it," Alberto replies quietly.

The train slows, but this time it's to deliver us to our destination, Aguas Calientes. Gathering our packs, Alberto and I jump off the train and onto the dusty platform. The station at Aguas Calientes is a three hundred-foot-long open-air structure. It has a mosaic rock floor, and a slanted, flat-topped fiberglass roof held up by a series of white painted steel pillars. At the far end of the station is an enclosed lobby area with rows of chairs and a small bar. Beyond the lobby and at the farthest end of the terminal are a few administrative offices where train schedules are posted and passenger luggage is stored.

Walking through the terminal and stepping off the back side of the station, we find ourselves dwarfed by the majestic peak of Putucusi, a 12,000 foot granite dome covered with lush tropical vegetation and speckled with shards of white and gray granite. At its summit, the pinnacle of Yanantin stands out against the horizon like a mighty platform of the Gods. According to locals in the area, the pinnacle of Yanantin is one of the ancient landmarks where the powers of the cosmos are harnessed to an earthly site. By the looks of this mammoth and majestic stone pillar, I do not doubt the legend for a second.

To our right is the Urubamba River. Roaring and foaming crystal-clear waters crash against its huge, smooth shoulders of granite. Walking along a footpath parallel with the river, we spot clusters of tattered dwellings made of wood, brick, mud and sticks. Children play in the bright sunlight on the river's boulders while their dark-skinned mothers wash clothes in the river. As we make our way downhill, three squealing piglets chase each other down the dirt pathway, veering around us like a river around its rocks. Their tiny curled and bouncing tails humorously lead the way to the open air marketplace just ahead. As we approach the area, the long faces and pitiful eyes of the vendors bore right into me, tugging on that part that wants to help the underdog. I walk *into* the marketplace with nothing but my backpack and I walk *out* with my arms full of sympathy purchases. My newly purchased booty includes two silkscreened shirts, a miniature carved puma (mountain lion) stone sculpture, a bottle of "pure" water, two rolls of film, two stubby bananas, a strange piece of green fruit and a tiny but costly stone-carved Inca God.

To our left and uphill is the Pueblo Hotel, where our friend Eliceu and his group are staying. The finest in Aguas Calientes, the Pueblo Hotel is a harmonious complex of sixty-six Spanish style bungalows overlooking the Urubamba River. Built among lush palm trees, ferns and flowering tropical plants, the buildings stand out like miniature haciendas. Rust colored ceramic tile roofs and exotic woods create a sense of simple splendor and functionality. The stone floor in the small, well-kept lobby is worn, yet shines brightly from careful polishing. Alberto steps up to the reception desk and speaks in Spanish to the young woman behind the counter. I pick up a few words of their rapid interchange and piece the conversation together. He is asking if our friend Eliceu has checked into the hotel. We learn that Eliceu has indeed checked in but left with a small group for Machu Picchu early this morning.

"Let's jump on a bus and head for the ruins. We'll meet him there," I say.

"Agreed," Alberto replies, grinning from ear to ear as we head for the door.

To get to the buses we travel down through the center of town. The main drag is marked by heavily soiled railroad tracks running through the middle of Aguas Calientes. On one side of the tracks makeshift buildings with a wide assortment of storefronts are nestled into the rocky hillside. Tour guide shops, travel agencies, pizza parlors, souvenir and curio shops bulge from the communal plaza structures. The other side of the tracks is similar, with the addition of the Urubamba River as it flows gently toward the mouth of the Peruvian Amazon.

Alberto and I follow the train tracks and wind our way to the far edge of the business district. There in front of us on the left side of the dirt road are four tour buses. The first bus in line is packed with tourists and appears to be ready to leave for the ruins. It is a dirty white color, riddled with dents and scratches and has large passenger windows that slide open sideways. The tires are large and worn down to the fabric. If I didn't know better I'd think this bus is related to the jetliner that delivered us to Cusco a few days earlier. I hold the driver's attention with my broken Spanish while Alberto purchases our tickets and returns to the bus. As we board the vehicle, I notice the driver's face is more weathered than his tires. His half-closed bloodshot eyes, however, worry me the most.

"Look, Alberto. Up on the mountainside you can see one of the buses zigzagging along the roadway. It looks like they're at least two thousand feet high!"

"Yes, and look how the bus is careening from side to side, Val Jon."

"Uh-huh," I sheepishly reply.

"And do you see how close it is coming to the edge of the road?

There doesn't seem to be any railing, does there?" he adds with a daunting twinkle in his eye.

"No. No, Alberto, I don't see a railing. I think we just need to have faith in . . . our driver."

As we travel up the mountainside at breakneck speed, I'm unprepared for the breathtaking view before me. From a thousand feet above the river, the three remaining buses on the outskirts of Aguas Calientes look like a trio of salt crystals lined up behind one another. At a particularly hairpin turn, the bus careens so close to the edge I can feel the tires lose traction. What both amazes and worries me is that our driver seems unconcerned.

As I look out over the valley, I am overwhelmed by the beauty of the Peruvian Andes and the mountains of San Miguel. These timeless granite monoliths have existed for eons before my own birth. I, in my smallish life, can capture only a fragment of the time these giants of the earth have endured. As I gaze in amazement, the sheer cliffs of stone seem to wear ancient, Godlike faces, with blazing eyes and timeless stares. Endless peaks of granite stand side by side, rippling off into the distance like ancient Inca warriors lined up for a final charge. In the dusty glass bus window, superimposed over the majesty of the moment, I catch an image of my own face. There in my beaming gaze is the boy who dreamed of coming to this place so many years ago. Into his eyes I am drawn. Into his heart I am woven. Here, in this moment of majestic reflection, there is no time. Eternity dances between "what was" so many years ago, "what is" in this very moment and "what shall be" in the distant future. Within this threefold, eternal dance, the time between childhood and adulthood takes not even a single heartbeat. In an instant, his young spellbinding dream is now my mature reality. Could all of eternity exist within just a single moment? Who's to say that time is real anyway? Perhaps we are so caught up in living our daily lives that we forget to honor the timeless aspects of life. We forget to notice the eternality of the stars in the heavens—the stars that were there when we were kids are the same ones that will be there for our children's children. We forget that there are not really four seasons in a year, but rather one constant movement of nature as it eternally cycles around the illusion we call time. We forget that although we can be hurt, wounded and even die, our spirits will never perish.

The pinnacle of Yanantin with the Urubamba River flowing around its base near the town of Aguas Calientes.

CHAPTER SIX

TRUTH:

THE THIRD DIMENSION OF KNOWING

Do you see the "truth" in the timeless lie?

The Inca fire, rain, earth and sky
illuminate quite clearly the timeless lie
In this moving stillness, I do confide
in anguish's shroud and joy's delight

It comes to me in this eternal now
the serious anticipation upon my brow
of finding the secret in this moment of grace
as we remember ourselves, face to face
with the astonishing truth of the timeless lie
Tell me now, do you see it as clearly as I?

The force of a frigid wind rocks me back into the Seat of the Condor. The golden moon hangs motionless at the zenith of the now thinly overcast night sky. The torch lights in the ruins far below have long since been extinguished, marking the end of my friends' ceremonies. For me, however, the ceremonies are just getting started. I can feel another dimension pulling me as I reflect on the lessons I have already received. *Humility* and

53

Eternality are right here in my experience. And although I am inspired by them, I fear I will have trouble holding more than just these two dimensions. Staying humble is a pretty tall order, let alone remembering that we are also eternal. Even though it will be a challenge to hold them both, I know it is exactly what I need to do. A wave of heat runs up through my body as the burn zone returns carrying its next message.

> *In the light of the Truth, seek not what you will never find—for your destiny shall be never to know in the way you desire. Rather, look directly into the Inca Fire and remember the truth of what has always been known.*

The words flow through me as I write them down. The sound of static electricity fills my ears as the *Inca Fire* blazes, beckoning me to step in. This time as I step, my memories transport me many years into the past for a vivid and profound experience of *Truth*.

I awaken with the force of a lightning bolt. Luminescent green numbers on my alarm clock flash 6:05 a.m. As I jerk upright in my bed, obscure shadows slowly change into coherent objects before my eyes. The ominous intruder near the door becomes the familiar brass coat rack. Still reverberating in my head are five haunting words whispered by a faceless dream-time orator, "Today, you meet the master." As I reflect on my lucid dream, I wonder if it's just my imagination or if someone is really trying to communicate with me. I'm more suspicious than trusting of such things, as I've been seeking truth for some time and haven't yet found it. I need tangible evidence to back up everything, especially dreams that have this kind of effect on me.

The year is 1975 and I am living in Kyoto, Japan with six other musicians. Our agent had booked us a three-month gig in a high-class nightclub in the downtown area. Kyoto is an ancient oriental city. From 794 to 1868, it served as the capital of Japan and the seat of the Imperial Court. It is also the home of gifted craftsmen, artisans, scholars and religious leaders who gathered there to create its grand cultural elements. Kyoto, being Japan's most spiritual city, contains over two thousand shrines and temples in addition to its astoundingly beautiful natural scenery. At the heart of Kyoto, the Emperor's castle stands majestically above all structures, as a reminder of authentic Japanese heritage and royalty. Buddhism is the predominant religion in Japan and wields a powerful influence at all levels of society.

It is a cold winter Sunday morning, and normally I would spend the day sleeping or sightseeing, but not today. My abrupt awakening from the disturbing dream suggests a different course of action. With mild anxiety, I get dressed and leave my small apartment. I soon find myself walking through the nearby graveyard toward the open market or "Ginza." Traversing headstones capped with rice cakes and tangerines, I approach the familiar outdoor produce stands. Brown and gray-cloaked elders flick snowflakes from their gnarled fingers as they grope through bundles of vegetables and fruits. Pinched faces and narrow eyes quickly dart away as I attempt to greet them. I drift aimlessly for an hour until it dawns on me I am lost.

Turning in circles in the middle of the street, I try to locate a familiar landmark—there are none. It's interesting, every time I get lost, I feel a need to immediately find my way. It's impossible to just allow myself to "be lost." It's apparent to me that my incessant need to have certainty and control over my life is, in this moment, totally overpowering. This control thing has its downside. It's like having a really stubborn child inside of me who has his own way of doing things and doesn't give a damn about what I want.

While standing in the middle of a bustling marketplace overflowing with fish carts and vegetable bins, a question comes to mind: could this control issue be what drives me to seek truth in my life? It makes sense. If I have possession of "truth" I'll have certainty, confidence and control. Yes. That's it. That's the truth. I'm now confident that—wait just a moment here—this feeling of confidence—it's because I think I've just found the truth, isn't it? Makes me feel good, doesn't it? Gives me certainty, right? So it stems from my need to control, right? Well that's depressing, because control is my problem in the first place. All right, enough of this garbage. Just forget the whole thing. This is where the quest for truth always ends up, in confusion and annoyance.

I decide to get a change of scenery and head up a cobblestone road toward the rising sun. Within a few minutes, off in the distance, I notice a man wearing a bright blue and green scarf walking toward me. As we approach each other, his features indicate that he is American or maybe European.

"American?" he asks in a British accent.

"Yes," I reply.

"You look a bit lost. Can I help you in some way?"

"I got turned around somehow. Everything looks the same to me," I say.

"Indeed, the landmarks are not easy to remember in Kyoto."

"Are you American, too?" I ask.

"English. I'm here on a concert tour. I'm a pianist."

"That's great. I'm also a musician. I play bass guitar in a rock band. I'm playing at 'Club Dominus' in downtown Kyoto," I reply.

"Well now, that's a coincidence. How about going for a cup of tea and a chat?" he asks.

"Sure. But I don't—"

"—know where you are? No problem. I know a little teahouse just around the corner," he says, confidently waving me on.

Without further conversation or introduction, we wind our way around narrow back alleys until we come to a small establishment wedged between two weathered apartment buildings. Colorful flags and rows of black vertical Japanese text adorn each side of the entryway. The door reminds me of an ancient Japanese pagoda with curved wooden planks and ornate carvings. The entryway is shorter than I expect, and I almost bump my head passing through. Although the doorway is obviously made for shorter people, I get the idea it is also designed to evoke humility from foreigners, kind of like a Zen architectural design—humility is ensured whether one bumps their head or not.

Upon entering, a petite young waitress immediately greets us. She wears a bright white kimono with pink flowers sewn into the fabric, and her thick black hair is gracefully pinned in a traditional bun. Turning to us and bowing constantly, she leads the way to a small table in the far corner of the tearoom. The smell of fresh herbs fills my senses. Bowing, she points toward a low, black lacquered table embraced by two well-worn dark green pillows.

"Domo arrigato, sumi masen," my host responds as he bows respectfully.

"Hai, dozo," she replies, bowing even lower than he and then quickly scurrying away.

Turning to me he asks, "Do you speak Japanese?"

"Scho shee ne hongo. I only speak a little," I reply.

"You have a good accent for a beginner. My name is Jacob," he says as he gently moves his hand across the table toward me.

"Val Jon. It's a pleasure to meet you Jacob," I reply shaking his huge hand.

Through our discussion I learn he is a concert pianist who travels the world playing music for dignitaries and royalty. Jacob is a man of great candor with a face filled with the kindness of a Bach lullaby. It's easy to tell he's a musician because he has an eccentric, creative look about him. During the next hour or so, we converse about music, philosophy, art, religion and life in general. Suddenly, in the middle of a conversation about truth, his voice takes on an eerie, familiar tone. At first I can't place it, but then abruptly it hits me. It sounds like the same voice I heard in my dream early this morning. Then he says something that stuns me.

"Val Jon, yesterday I played for Reverend Mumon Yamada, the most renowned Zen Master in all Japan. Given your interest in spiritual matters, perhaps today you should meet this master."

Mouth agape, I blink several times to ensure I'm awake. *Today, you meet the master,* roars in my head. "This is uncanny! Just this morning I heard those same words in a dream!" I blurt out.

"Marvelous. You have obviously received a spiritual calling. Please allow me to set up an appointment for you so you can meet this Master. He is one of the few teachers I have met who speaks the truth in a most profound yet simple way."

Before I can respond, Jacob pulls a sleek, gold-trimmed pen from his shirt pocket and draws a musical scale on his tea-stained paper napkin. With each line of the scale he puts a letter of his first name, so they look like musical notes arranged within a bar of music.

"I'll call the monastery and set up an appointment for you today at one o'clock. When you arrive, give the monks this napkin and they will grant you entrance to Reverend Mumon," Jacob states softly.

As I reach across for the napkin, my mind races with questions. How is it this is happening to me? What a freaky coincidence, that I hear words in a dream and then meet someone who repeats them to me. Can there actually be some form of communication that exists outside conventional means? And what about this "Master" who supposedly speaks the truth? How can this be a coincidence? It defies all logic and reason, yet I can't deny that it's happening.

"Val Jon, I'll also write the directions to Reverend Mumon's monastery so your cab driver will know how to deliver you. It's quite far from Kyoto, up in a remote part of the mountains, so you'll need to leave at once to get there in time. Mumon hosts guests daily at one o'clock, and you do not want to be late as he does not allow people in to his sanctuary after that time."

Stunned by the sequence of events, I cannot clearly recall how we parted, but prior to catching a cab I do remember stopping briefly in the Ginza to purchase a single red rose for the Reverend. Ducking into a tiny cab, I hand the driver the directions Jacob had written for me and wait for some understanding or recognition. *"Hai! Domo arrigato,"* he chirps, as we take off like a rocket. Because of the speed with which we're traveling, the only landmarks that stand out are more than a block long. The Emperor's Palace is one such sight. Located in the very center of Kyoto, this stone marvel's turrets spire far into the heavens, piercing the clouds with their samurai-like tongs. Monolithic snow-covered bronze statues of ancient warriors stand rigid guard inside the Emperor's gated courtyard.

Jacob was right when he said the monastery was remote. I've been traveling for over three hours on treacherous switchbacks cut into the side of the mountain. Dense forests surround me and wrap themselves around the snow-covered dirt road, creating a sparkling white artery of ice. Snow is falling so fast the cab's windshield wipers struggle to keep up. I find myself caught in a whiteout of blinding ice crystals and spinning snowflakes. Instead of reducing his speed, my driver opts for flooring it, staying as close to the inside edge of the road as he can. Although this strategy seems to work for him, I silently slip back into western religion.

"Just another way I try to maintain control," I chide myself out loud.

The cabby overhears me, slows down and quips, *"Wakat aniee?"* Which basically means, I didn't get what you just said, buddy, so would you repeat it for me, please?

"Di jobe, di jobe," I reply, which means, it's okay, relax, I'm just freakin' out back here.

"Hai dozo!" he snaps, flooring it again.

"Hey, bozo!" I think, in a moment of irreverence.

My head jerks back violently and sparks a flash of truth. There is really nothing I can do about this situation. If I'm destined to die, it will happen whether I like it or not. It doesn't really matter if I pray or curse. What will be, will be. To reduce my anxiety, I play visual tag with the Emperor's castle far off in the distance. My folly doesn't last long, however, as the landmark slowly vanishes in a crystalline white blizzard.

Further and further back into the wilderness we travel. It's now 12:30 in the afternoon. I have only half an hour left. We've got to be getting close to the monastery now. Then I have a flurry of doubts. What if this guy is lost and we wind up freezing to death? Or what if Jacob isn't really who he said he was? For all I know, he could be a practical joker. What about this cab driver? Maybe he's taking me for an extended ride to bilk me of my yen. Or worse, maybe he's going to rob me and leave me out here in the wilderness. There's no way of knowing the truth, it's all speculation driven by anxiety. The cab suddenly jolts to a stop. Whatever is going to happen, it's going to happen now. The cabby turns around and looks at me with a sardonic grin. I'm expecting the worst, when he matter-of-factly points to the fare meter for payment. Relieved, I hand him a wad of yen and he nods sharply, pointing to the passenger door handle.

Stepping out of the cab I barely get the door closed before he bolts away into the whiteness. In bewilderment I watch my only link with civilization disappear. Falling snowflakes quickly cover fading tire tracks, leaving me alone and uncertain. I push up the sleeve of my parka and check the time. It's ten minutes till one. Jacob had told me not to be late or the Master would not see me. But where is the monastery? With a sickening sensation in my gut I search the dense white forest for some indication of civilization.

Nothing! Not a building, not a statue, nothing. "It's got to be here somewhere. But where is it?" I moan.

Then I spot something in the blinding whiteness just ahead. When I peer into the landscape, a high wall made of white stucco comes into view. As I move closer, I realize it's a huge, rectangular fortress-shaped structure. I look to the right, and my eyes lock onto a colossal pair of ancient wooden doors. Gigantic greenish-tinted metal hinges stretch out and grip dark timbers like fingers from a massive Buddha. A coal-black iron ring hangs from each door, calling menacingly to mortal hands. Ten trembling fingers grip an ice-laden ring and tug.

The door slowly yields to my demands, and creaking hinges pierce the snowy serenity as I step into this sanctuary of truth. As I enter, four black swans take flight from a pond in the central courtyard. Jet black wings soar into the sky with Zenlike grace as they vanish into the icy heavens. Next to the pond is a three-story pagoda made of ancient wood with bronze adornments. Its curved beams and intricate patterns demand a measure of introspection and appreciation. Embracing the pagoda on three sides, nestled along the inner walls of the monastery, are thatched roof buildings. Sidewalks made of thick, ash-colored wooden planks extend from their front walls. Between the sidewalks and the pagoda, on all three sides, lie forty or fifty feet of rock gardens and finely manicured pathways. Peppered throughout the garden area are wise and serene-looking stone figurines.

With only minutes to spare, I notice an old woman standing on the sidewalk to my far left. Her face is aged and wrinkled yet her eyes shine with the joy of a newborn baby. Her gray, wiry hair is braided up around her red, frostbitten ears, and her back is severely hunched. Wearing a tattered brown gunnysack-shaped kimono, she holds an old, round, woven straw broom in her left hand. She looks up at me slowly and smiles, then extends a tiny wrinkled hand from her kimono, motioning me toward her. I follow her closely as she leads me to the third building on the left and opens its shoji doors. She gestures for me to remove my shoes before I enter. Bowing with gratitude, I comply and slowly step up into the antechamber.

A wave of warm air hits me as I enter the room. The floor covering is pearl-white and made of a tough woven fabric. The tan rice paper walls are adorned with colorful nature scenes, and the smell of sandalwood incense permeates the room. To my right, I spot two young monks who look like they're right out of the Zen Classics. Red frostbitten noses protrude from hooded black robes, two sets of small white fingers wrap themselves over the rim of a three-foot, ember-filled caldron. The monks greet me in an austere manner as I give them the rose I had purchased and the napkin that Jacob gave me.

"Why have you come?" one of them asks sharply in broken English. I think surely they will ask about the sound of one hand clapping, but they don't. I methodically recount my early morning dream and the sequence of events leading up to my arrival. Without any reaction or acknowledgment, the older monk picks up the rose and the napkin and abruptly leaves the room. Only a moment later, he returns and motions me to follow him down a narrow corridor. At the end of the hallway, two rice paper doors slowly slide open and my gaze falls immediately onto the face of Reverend Mumon Yamada.

In a split second, the Reverend takes inventory of my entire life. It's as if he is watching a movie of my life, learning everything there is to know about me. He sees where I was born, all the good and bad things I have ever done. He witnesses my rebellious teen years, all my fears, beliefs, desires, hopes and even my deepest aspirations. He even sees the time I talked little Trudi, my ten year-old sweetheart, into dropping her pants in our basement. Not only is he witnessing my life, the eerie thing is that he is also letting me in on the fact that he's doing it. As the transmission of images stops, Mumon's smiling face beams at me like a movie critic satisfied with a screening. I have never been so vulnerable in my entire life. I have nothing left to hide. He's seen it all. Although it's disconcerting, in a way it's also very freeing. There's nothing I *can* hide now. My anxiety about being found out by this remarkable Zen Master has vanished.

Collecting my thoughts, I steady myself and begin scanning the long narrow chamber. On each side of the room sit ten or twelve officials and dignitaries, many of whom appear to be of Japanese descent. After checking out the guests, my attention again returns to the Master. Reverend Mumon is a small man in his late eighties. He has wispy, thin, white hair and a silver mustache and goatee, and is wearing an orange muslin kimono. As a Zen monk, Mumon has no family, wife, property or home. Jacob had mentioned to me that he is known throughout Japan as a profoundly holy man who possesses a "spring breeze" about him rather than an austere "winter wind." It is said that he considers himself to be nothing more than a simple monk who serves his community. Looking at him, I can see the lighthearted spring breeze in his warm, shining eyes and his beaming face. Reverend Yamada Mumon holds great admiration for the Zen practices of Master Hakuin (1685–1768). And like Hakuin, he suffered from tuberculosis in his childhood. After a grim medical diagnosis, he turned to Zen as a means for curing his disease. As unbelievable as it may sound, he was cured within three years. This miracle compelled him to seek truth, and after years of severe training, he became a great Master.

Looking into the eyes of Reverend Mumon, it is clear to me why he has an excellent reputation. His reverent presence is undeniably humble. Rather than residing on a throne above others, this man sits cross-legged on the floor along with all of his distinguished visitors. As my view of the room widens, I suddenly see something that causes me to burst into uncontrollable laughter. There, on each side of him, pointing in his direction, are two state-of-the-art Sansui electric heaters. How incredibly funny and ironic this scene is. The monks outside are shivering over an archaic, coal-filled iron caldron to stay warm, while this fellow enjoys the wonders of modern technology. My laughter evokes shuns and faces of disdain from the guests. Their faces convey, "How disrespectful of this Westerner to display such amusement in the presence of a great Master."

Reverend Mumon, however, doesn't share the same reaction as his audience. Instead, he rolls with laughter and slaps his knees so hard he almost rocks over backwards. How wonderful to behold a revered Zen Master making light of his own indulgence. If I am to find truth, it most certainly will be here. Still chuckling and rocking back and forth, he motions me to take the last available seat on the far side of the room.

After speaking with a number of dignitaries, Mumon beckons me forward to sit in front of him. *Today, you meet the Master,* rings in my head again. I get up and walk to the shiny, black silk and gold-trimmed meditation mat on the floor in front of him. I take my place and bow in reverence. In my previous Zen studies, I read every possible scenario about master and student meetings. I want to impress him with the "right answers." The teachings of D. T.

Suzuki and Alan Watts race through my mind. Which koan is he going to hit me with? None come. Instead, his smiling wise eyes pierce through my childish ego and search the depths of my soul.

The connection is profound. Our initial greeting transpires without saying a word to each other. It's as if a speechless translucent dialogue is flowing between us. Then the Master breaks our gaze and reaches around behind his back with his left hand. As he pulls his hand back, I notice he holds the long stemmed red rose I had brought for him. He slowly brings the flower up to his nose and inhales deeply. His coal-black eyes twinkle with childlike delight.

With his right hand, Mumon motions me closer to him. I grab the sides of the mat with both hands and lurch forward until our knees touch. There is complete silence in the room and everyone's eyes are on us. He then turns his right hand palm up, extends his crooked index finger and beckons me still closer. Leaning far forward, my face is now less than a foot away from his. At this close range I can now see great detail in his kind face. Although in his eighties, he has the appearance of a child. His skin is weathered, old and wrinkled, and yet it has a remarkably youthful, vibrant glow. His skimpy silver beard converges an inch below his chin into a silly goatee and his black eyes sparkle with eternal wisdom. Without breaking eye contact, Mumon gently raises the rose and holds it right between our faces. Like two kids playing hide-and-go-seek, our gaze darts around the freshly-bloomed rose petals.

"Let us now address why you have come," he whispers in broken English. "You seek truth, yet doubt its existence. This is all right, because in your culture, more importance is placed on 'telling' the truth than on 'knowing' it. How can the truth be told if it isn't first known?" Before I can ponder his question, he continues, "You do not doubt truth as much as you doubt those who have espoused it. Rather than people asking you to tell the truth, it would be more honorable for them to ask you for what they wanted to hear. It is because of this deceit that you have become confused about the nature of truth."

Mumon makes perfect sense. That's exactly what happened. I

have had few experiences knowing the truth, and often felt I had to endorse the "truths" of others. Not only did it confuse me, it also drove me to place more credibility in others than I placed in myself. No wonder I have such low self-esteem. I bow and smile in acknowledgment.

"Let us now examine the real nature of truth. Truth is nothing more than 'what is, exactly as it is.' A lie, on the other hand, is taking 'what is' and trying to make it something it isn't. The moment we allow something to be as it is, with nothing added or taken away, we are in the presence of truth. Although this sounds simple, it is not easy to practice because 'what is' can be quite paradoxical."

He must have picked up on my confusion, because he clarifies his point. With his index finger extended, he alternately touches the rose petals and then one of the thorns protruding from the spindly stem. Eyes twinkling, he continues.

"Behold, the soft beauty of the petal and the sharp point of the thorn. 'Petals' and 'thorns' exist separately as I touch them. Yet they are not separate, because it is impossible to tell where 'petal' ends and 'thorn' begins. As both merge into the 'stem,' they become aspects of a single rose. So which is true? Are they separate things? Or are they one thing? The answer is they are both—and they are neither."

Here's the Zen koan. They are both and they are neither? It doesn't make any sense, and it isn't logical, but I somehow understand it. The problem is, this definition of truth doesn't help give me any more control, so of what value is it? He must have been able to read my mind because he responds immediately. Moving his index finger down to one of the thorns, he presses against it firmly until his flesh is indented. Although there is no blood, it looks painful. My first reaction is to come to his aid, but at some level I know not to move a muscle. As he continues to speak, I'm glad I didn't.

"And so here exists the paradox. Until you learn to manifest certainty within your own heart, truth will have little utility for you. Certainty and command do not arise out of truth itself. Rather they are born of our ability to embrace truth. Few embrace, many indulge. Let us examine the notion of pleasure and pain. While feeling the pain of the thorn, rather than embracing 'what is,' many avoid 'what is' by seeking 'what isn't'—in this case, relief in the form of pleasure. Those who indulge in pleasure try to make it last beyond its time as a way to avoid discomfort. Like the rose with the perfection of its petals and thorns, life is filled with the perfection of pleasures and pains. When we can embrace all experiences with equal respect, not just those we crave, command quickly follows."

Then, right in mid-sentence, he dives down into the bottom of his oversized kimono. What on earth is he doing? All I can see are tufts of white hair bustling around and popping up here and there. After a moment, he emerges holding a tiny pair of wire-rimmed glasses that are hinged in the middle. He had obviously stashed them in his kimono for occasions such as this. He reaches behind him again, but this time has in his hand a small paperbound book with a flower design on the cover. It's a book he has written called *A Flower in the Heart*. As he unfolds and positions the tiny lenses over his nose, he asks me my full given name. As I answer him, he writes in the front cover, *To Mr. Val Jon Farris from Rev. Mumon.*

When he passes the autographed paperback to me and bows down, I realize he is bestowing upon me not just a book, but a charge to return to America and encourage people to embrace everything, from the beauty of the petal to the pain of the thorn. I bow in return and graciously accept his gift. What happens next I will never forget. Reverend Mumon stands up and slowly makes his way to the rear of the room and picks up a large black and silver tray of cake and tea. Methodically, with incredible grace, he serves each of us a divine snack. I can't believe my eyes. A task normally left to the monks or servants, he does with great dignity and reverence. Here before me is a great Zen Master, who has dignitaries traveling the world to be with him, and he is serving *me* cake and tea. I reflect on times when I felt degraded because of the menial tasks I was asked to perform in my job. I now understand that dignity does not come from *what* one is doing, but from *how* one does it. The reverence of the moment has nothing to do with the actual act or task. Serving is a sacred act for Reverend Mumon because *he* creates it that way. The whole notion of being above certain tasks crashes down around my petty little ego.

After dining, the Master abruptly stands up and without a word, walks out of the room. All the guests are then gathered up by the two monks and ushered out the side door that leads to a garden. I stop to take a picture of an incredible black marble Buddha and then everything goes blank. The next thing I remember, I'm standing in front of the doorstep to my apartment back in Kyoto! I have no memory of the return trip. There is absolutely no recall of a cab, bus, auto, or any other form of transportation. It's as if a three-hour section of my life has literally vanished. To this day I have no idea how I got back to Kyoto that day. The truth of the matter is, I don't need to know—because it's clear to me that it just "is."

My time with Reverend Mumon Yamada taught me many things. Most of all, I learned that there are no absolute truths, that truth is relative depending on one's viewpoint. Going back to the rose analogy, from the position of the petals, the truth is sweet, from the position of the thorns, it is painful, yet from the perspective of the entire rose, it is both. So which is true?

This understanding about relative truth holds a great lesson for me. I recall many times in my life when I thought I knew the truth and others didn't, or vice versa. Another important realization is that personal freedom comes from appreciating and embracing everything life has to give. When I can include everything, from the sweetness of life to my own suffering, I am free. When I resist or try to change my suffering, I am trapped. Lastly, I learned that there are Masters on this earth who have transcended ordinary life and function in realms I can only dream of.

Val Jon Farris

As if no time passed since stepping into the burn zone, I find myself back at the Seat of the Condor, staring up into the night sky. My memories of Japan show me that truth does, in fact, exist within me. To access that truth I must, however, be willing to set aside what others believe or tell me to believe and look into myself. As I reflect on this insight, I also realize that the dimensions of *Humility* and *Eternality* and *Truth* exist in many events of my life, not just the profound ones at the top of mountains or with great Masters. For example, during my travels in Peru I became aware of a number of such events. I recall being deeply humbled seeing the little Inca girl from the train. My reflection in the bus window showed me the timelessness of eternity. It is clear to me now that I can identify when and where the dimensions are present, but I can also spot when and where they are *absent*. There is real value in this awareness, because when they're present I can deepen them, and when they're absent I can call them forth. I feel that I'm beginning to gain the insight and perspective needed to become my own "simple monk."

CHAPTER SEVEN

FROM AGUAS CALIENTES

TO THE GUARD SHACK

Fly me to the valleys of my ancestor's pain
Or high into the spires of a deity's flame
For wherever I go, I'll soar ever higher
Till I rise to the challenge of this Inca Fire!

"Val Jon, we're here. Let's get off the bus. We've arrived at Machu Picchu," Alberto says, shattering my eternal reflections in the bus window.

"Thanks Alberto. I was deep in thought. Unbelievable place isn't it?"

"Yes, it's just nice! A very spiritual place," he replies with great enthusiasm.

The bright blue Peruvian sky bathes the earth in a warm, luminous glow. The twenty or so people already at the site seem peaceful and respectful. Just to our left and uphill is the small fifty-room Machu Picchu Inn, built years ago to accommodate the first pilgrims. To the right of it, closer to the ruins, an open-air restaurant serves food. Under the metal roof, a hundred or so wooden tables can easily seat five hundred people. Next to the restaurant is a small booth for purchasing meal tickets. To our right and slightly downhill there's a long, narrow one-story building containing restrooms and a security room that visitors use to store their personal belongings while exploring the ruins.

We walk up the stone steps to the ticket booth and site entrance. The small fee they charge seems a paltry sum for gaining entrance to such an awesome place. In the small, narrow building a few feet to the left, a smiling attendant tears our tickets and motions us through the security station. On the other side, a stone pathway leads to the entrance to the ruins. To our right and far across the valley I see the pinnacle of Yanantin, a huge vegetation-covered granite dome standing high above the Sacred Urubamba Valley. Far below and in the distance, the Santa Ana railroad tracks glint in the sun as they snake their way around the dome's colossal base.

I approach the ruins, feeling as though I'm walking in a dream. The sensation inside my body is so profound I have difficulty staying with the reality of the moment. Is this really happening? Am I actually going to reach the place I dreamed about as a boy? With each step the dream becomes reality.

We slowly make our way through a mazelike passage of ancient stone walls leading to the interior of the ruins. The lush green grass growing around the ancient stepping stones below my feet reveals a mysterious paradox. My eyes catch the vivid contrast between the new and the old, between that which lives seasonally and that which endures forever. Side by side, vegetation and stone offer their paradoxical pathway to the sacred land of the Inca. This moment is incredible! Step by step, I travel through the labyrinth of reality as well as the maze of my mind. Where does one stop and the other begin? What demarcates reality from mind? Does my identity really stop at the edges of my skin, or can it be I am a part of what I see and sense? Could the notion of individuality be an illusion?

Touching the smooth and massive rectangular stone wall beside me answers my questions. As my fingers connect with this ancient place for the first time, it feels as if I have reached around and touched myself on the shoulder. There's an eerie kind of "welcome home" feeling pervading my senses. It's like going through old photos or memorabilia that I haven't seen in years, and suddenly coming across a pendant, ring, or some object that holds special meaning for me. Touching it evokes a warm flood of remembrance, a connection at a very deep and profound level—like coming home.

Alberto and I sit in the small, thatch-roofed hut just inside the ruins. Awestruck, we gaze silently at the incredible sights. To our left and uphill, carved into the stone peak is the House of the High Priest, the Temple of the Three Windows, the Principal Temple and the Intiwatana Altar. A massive, sculptured stone fondly called "The Hitching Post of the Sun" is the highest point in the ruins. To our right and slightly downhill are the Ceremonial Baths, the Industrial and Residential Sectors, the Three Doorways and the Place of Two Mortors. To our far right and descending steeply toward the gorge, the Agricultural Terraces are carved into the hillside. Terrace after grass-covered terrace, these marvels step their way down the mountain until they meet with the sheer cliffs of stone that fall straight down, two thousand feet below, into the Urubamba Gorge.

After twenty minutes of reflective silence Alberto asks, "Why don't we split up so we can each have our own experience?"

"That's a very good idea Alberto," I whisper back.

"Shall we meet, say, in a couple of hours?"

"Sounds good. Where shall we meet?"

"How about under the tree over there in the Central Plaza?" he asks.

"All right. Let's meet at about two o'clock."

"Good. I'll see you then, my friend. Have a great time."

"Yes, you too, Alberto."

There's something exciting about being on my own. My senses are sharp and my mind is clear. A fresh energy and awareness surfaces within me. It's a sense of connection with my environment and an attunement to larger unseen forces that are in play all around me. An indescribable "pull" takes over my sense of direction. The adventure is in full swing now. I know that when I feel the pull, I'm tapped into a power much greater than my own.

Rather than head for the most popular sites within the ruins, I walk toward the Industrial Sector, straight ahead and to the right of the Central Plaza. In the massive stone-walled area, I am fast immersed in a mythical labyrinth of ancient construction. The granite walls, irrigation trenches, roofless dwellings and endless array of deadened chambers both confound and enchant me. I crouch down in the middle of a small stone dwelling, imagining Inca workers sitting around a wooden table chewing coca leaves as they build an elaborate ceremonial decoration. Visions of brightly-woven fabric in the forms of the sun, birds, snakes, spiders and mountain lions appear in my mind.

Just around the corner I come upon the Place of Two Mortars. In an open-air rectangular room lies a gigantic solid stone floor with two deep, curved indentations. As I stoop next to them, my imagination again springs to life, this time with images of plants and seeds being ground down to a thick paste. I sense that the Inca workers are creating brightly colored paints and dyes for some kind of spiritual ceremony. In one indentation, the thick paste is jet black, and in the other, bright red.

It's here that I feel the pull most strongly. I stand up and turn around to determine its point of origin. Peering over the Residential Sector, I locate its source. Standing like a proud majestic parent, the summit of Wayna Picchu, a two thousand-foot granite spire, calls to me from the northern edge of the ruins. At the very top, a cluster of mammoth boulders stands together like a group of high priests in secret communion. That's the place I need to be in order to receive the *Light of the Masters*! Without hesitation I weave my way out of the stone labyrinth and head for the highest point inside the ruins, the Principal Temple.

In a few minutes I'm passing through the Principal Temple and entering the high lookout point that holds the Hitching Post of the Sun. Carved out of a gigantic piece of granite, it has a smooth, otherworldly appearance. Curved steps and a square pinnacle adorn its mystical crest. According to legend, the Incas used the altar as a cosmological clock and metaphorically "tied the sun" to it during winter solstice in order to bring the warmth and light back. I reach out and touch the altar with my left hand. I don't feel anything special until I turn and look up at the high summit of Wayna Picchu. The line of sight between the two points triggers another mysterious vision. I suddenly see images originating long ago of two Inca priests making a "remote connection" with each other. One priest stands high up on the summit of Wayna Picchu looking down, and the other is here at this very spot where I stand. I can't get a feel for what transpires between them, but I sense it has something to do with a premonition of tragedy or despair. Then without further insight, the image vanishes as voices command my attention.

I turn to see who's talking, and spot a small group of English-speaking tourists gathered around a young local guide. He explains to them that the trail up to Wayna Picchu is closed to the public. I move closer and listen intently. He says a recent fire and subsequent flooding washed out portions of the trail, and because much of it is carved into sheer cliffs along the face of the mountain, the climb to the summit is now treacherous. He finishes by recounting a grim tale of a tourist who, just a few weeks earlier, had ignored the warnings and fell two thousand feet to his death. As a result, the officials closed the trail to the summit and posted security guards to deter risk-takers.

It never fails. I always want to do things that wind up breaking the rules. Given this news, I'll need to find a way around the tight security.

It's now two o'clock and time to meet Alberto. I scan the grounds around the tree in the center of the Central Plaza but don't see him anywhere. I soon locate him high atop the upper terraces as he's waving his arms in the air. I wave back, and start to climb the endless stone stairway. We meet halfway and turn toward the Principal Temple and the Hitching Post of the Sun. It's now time to plan how we will proceed with our evening. The sun is still high in the sky as Alberto and I pick a spot on the corner of a terraced ledge. Sitting right on the edge of the terrace enables us to dangle our legs and tap our heels on the lower stone wall.

"Will you be joining us tonight for the spiritual ceremonies?" Alberto asks.

"No I don't think so, Alberto. I'm going to be up there tonight," I reply, pointing in the direction of the Wayna Picchu summit.

"Oh, man. That's a big climb. Are you coming back down later or planning to stay the night up there?"

"I'm going to stay the night. It's the place I need to be in order to experience the *Light of the Masters*."

"Very good, Val Jon. That will be a great place to be."

"You are welcome to come with me, Alberto."

"No. I'm not quite as adventuresome as you. I'll stay down in the ruins tonight."

"Okay, then how about if we meet up in the morning?" I ask.

"Yes. Let's meet right here at, say, nine-thirty?"

"Sounds good to me. Will you let Eliceu know so he can come with you?"

"Yes. I'll tell him our plans when I see him this evening."

"Have a great time, Alberto. I'll be thinking of you tonight. In fact, I'll probably be watching you from up there."

"Please be careful, Val Jon, and good luck to you."

"Thanks, Alberto. Same to you. I'll see you in the morning."

It is now almost three o'clock. I should start my climb soon if I'm going to make it to the top before dark. I estimate a good three hours to reach the summit. But first I must study the moves of the security guards.

From the Hitching Post of the Sun, I survey the lay of the land. Just ahead is the north end of the Central Plaza. On its eastern flank lay the Residential Sector and two thatch-roofed structures that mark the beginning of the trail leading to the security fence and up to Wayna Picchu. To the left of the two structures is the Sacred Rock, a huge oblong stone that appears to have been planted into the ground at the far end of the Central Plaza. Directly behind the Sacred Rock is a low mountainous peak standing in front of Wayna Picchu. Because it looks like a child standing at the feet of a parent, I deem it "Mini Picchu." Its back side forms a saddle that merges with the lower front face of Wayna Picchu. To the right, a green guard shack is built squarely against Mini Picchu's rocky shoulder. A six-foot-high, barbed wire security fence runs from the shack's right front corner all the way to the cliff of the Urubamba Gorge, totally cordoning off the area.

I spot two security guards in the immediate area. One is permanently posted to the left of the Sacred Rock. The other guard is mobile and walks a path from the shack, out between the two thatched buildings toward the Central Plaza, along the western edge of the Residential Sector and back to the shack. It takes about six minutes for him to complete his beat. If I'm going to succeed, I will need to evade both guards, climb over the left side of the guard shack and find shelter on the trail around the right shoulder of Mini Picchu—all in less than six minutes.

I descend from my lookout post and make my way across the Central Plaza and up into the Residential Section. Beyond The Three Doorways, I travel to the eastern ridge of the ruins. I walk northward on the inside of a three-foot-high stone wall, parallel with the Urubamba Gorge, until I come to the north edge of the Residential Section. The guard shack is less than a hundred feet away, but to get there I have to traverse a vulnerable open area that runs behind the two thatch-roofed structures. There is a chance that one of the two guards will spot me as I attempt to cross. There's always a certain element of risk in matters like this. I may be able to reduce the risk by timing my actions according to the mobile guard's moves, but it will be luck or fate that keeps me from being spotted by the guard standing near the Sacred Rock.

I peer around the edge of a low irrigation wall, looking for the mobile guard. He has just passed the two thatch-roofed structures and is heading toward the Central Plaza. That gives me about five minutes. What about the other guard? I can't see him from my position, so I'll just have to risk it and hope he's looking in another direction. My heart pounds and the blood rushes through my temples. "Trust the process, Val Jon. The truth is, if you're meant to be at the top of that summit tonight, you'll be there. Be more committed to the truth than to what you want." The words have a familiar ring from lessons learned in my distant past. Without another moment's hesitation, I sprint with all my might out into the open.

CHAPTER EIGHT

PASSION:

THE FOURTH DIMENSION OF KNOWING

Down through the ages I come again and again
Into the hearts of beasts, sages, women and men
Casting every dark shadow, then striking with light
Waking my souls to meekness and might

Healing and wounding and tossing you about
Between the bliss of faith and the curse of doubt
The tender of souls imprisoned yet free
For I am who I am, and forever I'll be
Moving down through the ages and back into me

Rays of golden moonlight illuminate granite shards around the Seat of the Condor. Terrestrial shadows lay motionless under the dim light as the wind whispers its secrets into the silence of night. From within a slender crack in my imagination, a spark emerges. The *Inca Fire* again bursts forth to lead me into the next dimension of knowing:

The sun and the moon and the stars make tonight not the master's light, but the illusory light of hope, inspiration and illumination for mortal eyes to finally ask, And from whence does this radiant

77

golden beauty arise? And so, behind the moon, within the sun, and throughout the stellars bright, the Light of the Masters evokes its Passion from the essential nature of all things—sparked by the paradoxical desire to expand, yet the need to belong, by the orbits of freedom and the gravity of grace, by the force of mystery and the comfort of certainty, by the curse of doubt and the bliss of faith. The Light of the Masters is evoked by the union of compassion and fear, the tension between creation and destruction, and the dance between life and death. It is born of the force which draws the stars apart and too holds them together, by the poles of eternity, matter and space.

Again, I find myself stepping into the burn zone. As I gaze into the blazing flames, vivid images from my past consume me. Memories cascade around me and strong vibrations fill my body, leading me into the dimension of *Passion*.

The late morning sun shines on my face as the frigid wind rips across my numb cheekbones. The sensation of the sun's warmth coupled with the pounding winter wind casts me into a paradoxical sort of bliss. On one hand, the sun's rays bring a smile to my goggle-covered eyes, and on the other, the cutting wind contorts my lips into a frozen gargoyle-like grimace. Adding to the dilemma, the vibration of the Harley-Davidson beneath my rump threatens to drive me into a multiple personality if I don't dismount soon. The year is 1994 and I am out on a joy ride in the Southern California desert near Palm Springs. On this trip, I intend to have some fun and spend a few days communing with nature. Shifting down to fourth gear, I scan for the entrance to the park.

The "park" I am about to visit isn't your usual family campground. Joshua Tree National Park is a half-million acres of rough desert terrain carved out centuries ago by the movement of glaciers. Huge red rock outcroppings jut from barren desert mesas, creating an unworldly scene. The Joshua trees are a strange cross between a cactus plant and a tree. Their green and brown limbs, covered with prickly spines, look like blessed arms reaching for the heavens. The word "Joshua" means "Jesus" and the trees eerily mimic images of the crucifixion.

Long shadows cast by the winter sun silently track my bike's forward movement. Just ahead on the right is the entrance I'm looking for. Leaning into the turn, I follow the dirt roadway a few hundred yards to the visitor's station. My "visitor experience" involves signing in, listening to the cautionary warnings, agreeing to a list of public safety rules, and receiving a park map for navigation. After my orientation, I jump back on my bike and head for the remote part of the park. Twenty minutes or so later, I pull into a small dirt parking lot. My bike is the only vehicle in the area, so I pull up close to a long, rusty iron chain that separates the empty lot from the desert. Dismounting, I pull the ignition key, lock the front wheel and unhook my black canvas day pack from the chrome sissy bar. After checking my water supply and provisions, I don my pack and leap over the low-slung chain and onto virgin golden brown desert sand.

After a few hours of walking in the open desert, all evidence of civilization vanishes and I find myself surrounded by massive rock formations and countless prickly, green and brown Joshua trees. I trek toward the afternoon sun, and soon become scissored between two converging mountain ranges. The ground is rocky and steep as I hike to a convergence point. Stepping out to the far edge, I notice the landscape drops into a deep ravine and the hillsides are covered with boulders and caves. I pull out my visitor map and turn it in every possible direction, trying to locate my position. There's an old, dilapidated mineshaft at the bottom of the ravine, so I use it as a reference point, and finally find my position. It isn't good news. I had crossed over into a red-tinted area on the map, labeled *Danger—Restricted Zone—Do Not Enter.* I am inside one of the most dangerous areas in the park. Part of my safety briefing included avoiding any terrain with "cavelike openings," as they belong to wild animals—including mountain lions.

I scan the terrain around me, and sure enough I spot cat tracks and fresh dung piles. Crouching low to the ground, I hesitate for a few moments before reacting. I had planned this trip in the first place to commune with nature. Being out here and serving myself up to the wisdom of the earth is my way of connecting with spirituality and the divine. Being part Cherokee, I am passionate about honoring the full spectrum of life, which includes embracing everything from the primal to the divine. It just so happens that "primal" is on the menu today. Fortunately, the Italian part of my heritage kicks in, compelling me to get the hell out of here before I become the meal.

I stand up and look around to determine my options. Suddenly I get an uneasy "pull" at the center of my torso. The best way to describe the sensation is directed intuition. The pull is strongest toward a massive rock formation about a hundred yards due west. Traveling toward it, away from the caves, feels like the right thing to do. As I come close to the rock, I make out some details. It's approximately thirty feet high and probably twice as wide. A giant vertical crack runs down through its solid stone face. The smell of damp earth draws me to the gaping crack in the stone. Before I know it, I'm climbing up into the opening and sliding my body sideways into its darkness. Cool damp air fills my lungs as soft tentacles of fern and fungi brush my left cheek. As the light diffuses and fades around me, the crack narrows, leaving little room to breathe. Inch by groping inch, I slide into the darkness until I spot a sliver of light a few feet ahead. Encouraged, I press on until the crack begins to widen and merge with the outer surface of the stone. I step out of the fissure, to stand at the edge of a magnificent circular clearing. This place is completely secluded and looks as if someone has purposefully landscaped it. It's amazing. The ground cover and plants appear manicured; the rocks and stones seem to be placed with remarkable balance and aesthetics in mind.

To my left, at the edge of the grassy area, I notice a strange looking boulder. It stands approximately eight feet tall and six feet wide, and has a smooth flat surface with an image etched on it. I move closer to get a better look. The image is that of a cross which seems to be formed from natural creases or "folds" in the stone. It's symmetrically perfect, with bisecting vertical and horizontal lines. I place my right hand on the surface of the stone. Warm to the touch, it sends me into a melancholy state, cradling me in a parental kind of embrace—one in which I feel safe, cared for and totally protected.

I pull myself out of the symbiotic stupor and walk around the boulder's left side. The landscape opens to an expansive mesa loosely embraced by two huge mountain ranges. In the center of the desert floor, about five hundred yards ahead, a rock formation juts up like a massive stone cathedral. The formation eclipses the setting sun, casting a shadowy, inviting path. With less than an hour of light left, I search for a safe place for the night. I quickly locate a spot on a rocky, mountainous ledge near the cathedral, about thirty feet above the desert floor. Although it won't provide cover during the night, I'll be able to spot predators easily if they approach.

From my perch, I have a panoramic view of heaven and earth. As night falls, the blackness of space is ablaze with millions of bright stars. A vast pincushion of light fills the void of velvety black space above me. How many eyes have gazed upon this panoply of celestial bodies? How many hearts and souls have been humbled by the infinite mysteries of the universe? Surely there are more stars than eyes that have perceived them—or could there be an equal number of eyes, on other worlds, looking up just as I am at this moment, asking the same questions? I shall never know the answer.

My eyes glide down from the heavens, past the horizon and into the shadowy desert floor looming below. Phantom creatures swirl around jagged starlit crags, drawing me into a vortex of unbridled fear and paranoia. How strange that in one moment I am inspired by the vastness of space and in the next I am terrified by the mysteries of the earth. As my eyes adjust to the darkness of the desert floor, the threatening phantoms transform into benign tree stumps, rocks and plants. With a sigh of relief I settle back onto the hillside and close my eyes—a terrible mistake.

I bolt awake with a blast of terror. The musky smell of wild beast fills my nostrils. I *never* should have allowed myself to drift off to sleep, *especially* in mountain lion country! The blinding darkness yields no certainty. I listen intently for the sound of movement. Then, directly behind me, maybe ten or twelve feet away, I hear the terrifying sounds of sliding rocks and clicking claws. Bloody images of torn flesh and flailing body parts rip through my mind. In the absence of breath, I hang in a vacuous moment awaiting the kill. One heart pound, two heart pounds, three heart pounds—then total silence as the cat stops pacing. Wedded in this eternal moment are predator and prey, engaged in the mortal question: *who* will make the *first* move?

What will it be? Should I run for my life and let the cat bring me down like a fleeing rabbit? Should I try to creep away slowly and delay the inevitable? Or should I stand my ground and put up a fight? My mind races to find a way out. Escape has *always* been an option. Surely I can craft *one more* escape without paying the price for taking a risk. Escape is a blessed curse. If I find a way out of this, I can revel in having avoided it. But the moment I escape, I become snared by the tyranny of knowing that someday there *will be* justice. It looks like that day is now upon me. Perhaps it's time to let go of trying to escape. Perhaps it's time to accept responsibility for my heedlessness. In truth, I've placed myself in this situation and, in so doing, I offer myself up as a feast for the beast. The question is, can I gather enough courage to accept my fate?

Wedged between terror and surrender, I have an insight. *I'm getting exactly what I asked for!* I had come out here to immerse myself in the natural world, which means embracing *everything* nature has to offer. It would be sacrilegious to bow out now. Surrender is my only course. Without another thought, I whip my body around toward the darkness. In a clear but calm voice I say, "I surrender myself to you." As my statement rings out, rocks scatter and tumble toward me. The cat pierces the deadly silence with a screaming growl. My heart races, pounding my chest as I steady myself for the attack. As one terrifying moment turns to the next, sweat pours from my chilled brow. My eyes search the darkness. There it is! Just to my right and about ten feet uphill darts a stealthy shadow. Frozen, I lock in on two luminescent green eyes peering straight back into my soul. But to my amazement, instead of leaping forward, the cat turns away and vanishes into the darkness. The wind bristles across my sweat soaked face and, more terrifying than being eaten by a mountain lion, I hear a clear, strong voice say:

It is not the beast you must surrender to. Look above you into the heavens. What do you see?

Stunned, I gaze into the night sky. There at the zenith I spot a dazzling crosslike constellation of stars. I can't believe my eyes. It looks just like the cross I saw folded into the strange flat stone back in the secluded meadow. The position and size of its two sections are proportionately exact. Chills run through my body and the hair stands high on the back of my neck. Examining the constellation, I count the number of stars. There are thirteen in all, six on the horizontal axis and six on the vertical axis. Where the two intersect, one additional star blazes with diamondlike intensity. The voice continues:

Behold the revelations of Spiritus and the Cross of Light and surrender yourself to their wisdom.

"Surrender? What do you mean? Who are you anyway? What is Spiritus? And what is the Cross of Light? Are you talking about Christianity? Church? What?" I ask pointedly.

The only reply I get is the desert wind that gently whips through the rocky crags around me. The skeptical part of me immediately doubts the authenticity of this ethereal message. After all, it could just be coincidence with a little of my creativity thrown in. Another part of me is intrigued, as I have had some unique spiritual encounters that were hard to explain through conventional wisdom. Still another part is deeply disturbed by the idea of surrendering to a cross. Although I have always believed in God, the notion of being a sinner from birth never sat right with me. It's not that I am down on religion, because I think it does a great service for many people. It's more the dogmatic idea of needing salvation before ever doing anything wrong that doesn't make sense to me. The other thing that disturbs me is all the fighting over who is the "one" God. It seems to me that God is big enough to take the liberty of manifesting in multiple forms. Besides, what if all the deviations of faith in the world are just God's way of honoring diversity?

I need more clarification before jumping to conclusions. I also need some time to shake off the terror still reverberating in my chest from the close call I had with the mountain lion. I've been in some tight spots in my day, but that one beats them all. Standing up and stretching my body helps in dispelling the tension. As I look up and scan the sky, I begin to question the ethereal voice I heard just after the lion fled. I need a convincing sign to prove that the voice wasn't just my imagination.

"If it's true I need to surrender to this cross, give me another sign," I spout. Silence, stillness, silence . . . "Wow!" I gasp, sitting back down abruptly.

At that very moment, a shooting star races across the middle of the constellation. I can't believe my eyes. I rub them briskly and gaze up again. Could it also be a coincidence? I can push the issue, but why not at least open to the possibility that some kind of revelation *is* occurring?

"Tell me what it means to surrender to the cross," I ask again. There is no reply. The desert wind blasts me with a wave of chilled air that pierces my jacket.

"Brrrrrr." Being trapped inside this frail body certainly has its disadvantages. Stars, on the other hand, can easily endure the frozen vacuum of space. Wouldn't it be great if I could be like a star? That's it. "I know what surrendering to the cross means!" I exclaim.

Although surrendering to the cross has strong Christian connotations, I sense something more fundamental is implied. As

I look up at the constellation, a flood of insights come to me. The first has to do with the symbolic meaning behind the cross's horizontal and vertical axes. Like stars that are impervious and virtually immortal, the *vertical* aspect represents all things divine and eternal. The up-down position of its axis serves as a spiritual grounding rod connecting heaven and earth. This aspect of the cross includes faith, grace, surrender and unity. The *horizontal* aspect symbolizes the frail and mortal physical body, and all things human and temporal. Its left-right orientation represents the arms outstretched into the toils of everyday life which involves identity, emotion, intellect and will. These insights are not completely new to me as I recall having read about an ancient Chinese symbol called The Cross of Woton, which possesses similar interpretations and is related to the notion of Yin and Yang, or complementary opposites. Other similar interpretations also exist in ancient cultures such as the Australian Aborigines, the Mayans, the Aztecs and the Inca.

The next insight concerns the central star in the middle of the constellation. As it shimmers within deep velvet blackness, it seems to be the hub for all the other stars. Following along the interpretations for the two aspects of the cross, I realize that the central star represents the turbulent nexus between humanity and divinity. Down through the ages this enigmatic nexus has sparked a multitude of wars, campaigns and crusades. On a personal level, its paradoxical nature drives us into confusion, denial, fear and ambivalence. The central paradox lies between the weakness of being only human, and our aspirations to be Godlike.

I can see where I have achieved "humanhood." Being possessive, petty, lustful, happy, sad, willful, etc., come easily to me. I have no problem being mortal. The Godlike side is another story. Although I have experienced a sort of "eternalness" and selfless humility, the bliss never seems to last very long. For a few years I immersed myself in meditation and prayer and abstained from desires, but when the phase was over, I wound up going hog wild into indulgence. I've even tried a third option of being both human and divine. My strategy entailed blending them together into a compromise of "not too human" and "not too divine." The result was a homogenized, passionless period in my life. It's that phase when, although we have our nasty little problems, we try to be truly good and loving, but it just doesn't seem to work for long.

This paradoxical struggle between humanity and divinity also produces a polarization of values within society. On the extreme "divine" side, there are those who abhor primal instincts and choose instead to live in total love and bliss, or so they say. They are the hypocrites of the world and judge anything that doesn't fit within their moralistic "holier-than-thou" ideals. On the extreme "human" side are those who opt for total indulgence. They are the "piglets" of the world. No trough is below them, and anything spiritual is not worth consuming. Between these two extremes lie those who vacillate back and forth or try to strike a balance through compromise. These three approaches do little to resolve the eternal paradox that exists at the center of the cross.

If these three options don't work, then what will? Looking up again into the constellation, I imagine the crucifixion of Christ superimposed over the thirteen stars. I have another flash of insight. Maybe resolving the paradox requires a kind of death, a kind of personal crucifixion if you will. The notion triggers a strange and intriguing question.

"What must die within me in order to fully live the challenge of being human *and* divine?" The answer that comes floors me.

"Your mediocrity," rings inside my head.

"My mediocrity! What do you mean my mediocrity?" I bark at the sky. Again, there is no answer from my invisible and now arrogant host.

"This really bothers me," I snap. "If you're gonna tell me something like that, at least you could explain yourself." There is no reply.

I'm definitely not being mediocre in my reaction. The emotional turbulence inside me does, however, jolt me into thinking about the reply I got. What could it possibly mean? To me, mediocre means blasé, apathetic, or even pathetic. I don't consider myself blasé, so why would that come as the answer to my question? After a few moments of musing, it dawns on me. Maybe the mediocrity has to do with not staying fully in touch with my divinity *while* I experience my humanity. In other words, rather than just getting angry about being called mediocre, what if I could stay humble *while* I'm angry? In this way I could exercise the divine attribute of humility while I indulge in my hot-tempered humanity.

My perspective shifts. The darkness is brighter, the stars are clearer and my senses are heightened. I have the realization that surrendering to the cross is about passionately embracing the paradoxical nature of life. The challenge is to value and embrace pleasure *and* pain, gain *and* loss, joy *and* sorrow, faith *and* doubt, even anger *and* humility. This way of relating to life is contrary to the notion of either avoiding or rising above our misfortunes. Essentially, the challenge is to keep a foot in both worlds and open fully to the stretching and turbulence it yields.

Why would anyone want to open fully to being pulled in two opposing directions? Wouldn't it be easier to go for compromise or minimize strife? Sure it would be easier, it's called mediocrity.

As I push back into the hollow of the desert mountainside an image comes to me of when I was a boy playing hide-and-go-seek with my friends. I recall "home base" being the big oak tree in my best friend Johnny's front yard. Someone would be designated as "it," and then would close their eyes and count to fifty while everyone else found hiding places. The object of the game was to reach home base without getting spotted by whoever was "it." What stood out in my memory was that there was always someone who wouldn't stray far from the tree for fear of getting tagged. The story was always the same. The kid would successfully avoid being "it," but constantly whined about not having any fun.

Looking up at the constellation again, it's now clear to me that the cross symbolizes living fully, taking risks and embracing absolutely everything that comes to me. It doesn't mean, however, that I have to *like* what comes, rather, I can trust that even my biggest misfortunes have a rightful place in my life. The constellation also doesn't mean I need to avoid compromise or resist taking a middle road from time to time. Rather, I should realize that the degree to which I am willing to step out in life and stretch myself is the degree to which I will experience the passion of being alive. With this approach, I'm assured of either being humbled into humanity or inspired into divinity, a win/win situation. What a great notion: to be passionate about every moment and every experience, to be daring and bold, and to know in my heart of hearts that all history, all events—even the most profane ones—are not only meant to be, they are sacred as well.

Laying my head back against the cold desert earth and opening my arms wide, I gaze upon the brilliant constellation one last time. Something tells me there is much more to this *Cross of Light* and this word, *Spiritus,* than was revealed to me tonight. There are much deeper secrets yet to be revealed. Perhaps it's not the right time, or maybe I'm not quite ready to see or hear them. Since I didn't get eaten by the mountain lion, I've still got some time to explore such mysteries. Someday I will return to this place so I can open myself to the revelations held within these stars. Until then, I will passionately stretch out onto the "cross" of my own life.

As my memory of being in the desert vaporizes, the Seat of the Condor provides a sense of support and solitary comfort. The *Light of the Masters* has now endowed me with four dimensions of knowing. It is this fourth dimension, *Passion,* however, that most inspires me. Its paradoxical nature casts me into a turbulent realm, encompassing the widest possible embrace between desires of the flesh and aspirations of faith. *Passion* brings my heart to the divinity of my soul. It infuses life and spirit into all the other dimensions. *Passion* forges *Humility* into tenderness, *Eternality* into resilience and *Truth* into the grandeur of art, integrity and aesthetics. *Passion* is a wonderful dimension that I will embrace with all of my heart and all of my soul for as long as I live.

CHAPTER NINE

FROM THE GUARD SHACK TO MINI PICCHU

The wetness of thunderclouds upon my face
Eternal tears flow down with grace
Into the sacred pool of this huaca's bowl
Evaporating slowly into the Inca soul
Evaporating fully into the passionate whole

With all my might, I sprint past the two thatch-roofed buildings toward a rocky area left of the guard shack. As I approach the small building, I spot the mobile guard as he walks toward the Central Plaza. Fortunately, the other guard is out of sight. Leaping up, I grab an indentation in the rock and pull myself up and over the high shoulder of stone and drop down to the back side of the guard shack. I move quickly to the outside corner where the barbed wire fence attaches to the structure, and peek around the corner to see if I can spot the mobile guard. He's just about to swing back around and head for the Residential Sector. I'm not home free yet. Bolting down the trail, I see a clump of tall grass growing between the embankment and the path. I lunge into the weeds and lay absolutely still so as not to attract attention. My heart pounds in my chest and my lungs are on fire.

After catching my breath, I roll onto my right side, and peer behind me to check on the guards. The coast is clear. Next, I focus my attention on the terrain up ahead. The trail shoots up at a forty-five-degree angle as it curves around Mini Picchu's right flank. The challenge is to climb the remaining three hundred feet or so without being seen. Not only will I need to evade the two security guards, but because the path ahead is completely exposed to the ruins, I'll also need to evade anyone else who might see me. Rolling over onto my back, I do a fast clothing check. Anything white or shiny will give me away. My bright white socks will have to go. I quickly remove my boots and socks, tuck the socks into my jacket pocket and put the boots back on over my bare feet.

Pausing at a low spot on the trail, I determine the best route forward. Approximately three feet in width, the path is composed of weathered flat stone steps, damp earth, weeds and loose rocks. On its left side is the almost vertical slope of Mini Picchu. Its rough granite surface is peppered with foliage and stone outcroppings. Just to the right of the trail is a narrow, two-foot grassy channel that grows between the path and the sheer cliff which tumbles off into the valley far below. The good news is I've breached the security fence without being detected. The bad news is that my *only* cover is on the grassy channel next to the abyss.

My green jacket blends well with the tall weeds as I work my way up the grassy area. Because of the high altitude, I have to stop every so often and catch my breath. Face to the dirt, I inhale the pungent grasses and the earthy fragrance of Peruvian stone. Turning my head to the right, I catch a glimpse of the abyss next to my right knee. My stomach sinks and I impulsively clutch a protruding rock.

"Keep moving. This is *not* a place to stop," I counsel myself. "All part of the experience," I add with a chuckle.

There, on the left side of the trail, just ten feet ahead is a two-foot round hollowed-out section of granite in the Mini Picchu hillside. Its rough, chipped interior surface looks as if it's been carved by hand. It'll provide cover for me while I catch my breath and plan my next move. Rolling across the pathway like an infantry soldier, I dash for the stone alcove. Turning my body sharply and thrusting it back into the opening, I slam to an abrupt stop. My backside fits perfectly into the hollow. I allow my head to gently fall back and touch the stone. As my breathing slows, euphoria sweeps through my body, like the sensation of well-being after a good workout or a fast run. To add to my glow, just inches in front of me, a broad, thin, horizontal sheet of sunlight intermixes with creased shadows. The illuminating display is caused by the afternoon sunlight as it sweeps by the jagged, outer edge of the alcove. Small ridges of stone shape the streaming sunlight into ribbons of alternating light and shadow. Tiny illuminated particles of dust dance in the light as they respond to my breath.

I pull my knees up to my chest and peer around the edge of the rock. The coast is clear. No one has spotted me. Pushing back into the hollow and exhaling deeply, my feeling of relief is abruptly consumed by a dizziness. I close my eyes and immediately see a fluttering of vivid colors and nondescript images. Then out of the blackness, a vision of red and yellow flames bursts forth. Hidden within the ribbons of fire I see a dark figure. The image slowly moves closer and the flames dissipate. In the clear black space, I see a native man sitting with his knees tucked up to his chest. He's turned sideways to me so I can easily see his profile. I sense he is some kind of holy man or priest. His eyes are blazing black and his graying hair is double-braided down his naked back. At the ends of each braid are tiny, brightly-colored threads laced into the tips of his hair. Just to the right side of his braids, two huge grayish feathers are attached by their quills to the back of a thinly woven red, green and black headband. His frame is small and frail, and he has multiple scars and blemishes over his entire body. He is wearing only a small tattered brown wrap around his waist and his feet are caked with dirt and heavily callused. A closer look reveals his short, stubby toes and dark yellow, severely cracked toenails. In his left hand, he holds a small stone-carved bowl with a wide-open rim and, in his right hand, he carries what appears to be a polished wooden walking staff.

I press my grass-stained palms hard onto my closed eyes to shake the image, but it only becomes more vivid. Suddenly the vision fills my body, as if this virtual priest has entered my torso and is perfectly mimicking my posture. His hands are within my hands. His head within my head, and even his gnarled bare feet are visible through my weathered brown leather boots. Leaning forward to disrupt the vision, I catch a glimpse of the ruins of Machu Picchu. There is something very strange about my perception. I'm seeing images superimposed over my regular sight. It's like having double vision, with one set of eyes seeing normally and the other somehow viewing what this Inca priest had witnessed centuries ago. I shake my head back and forth but it makes no difference. Among the stone temples and the Central Plaza I see a band of natives engaging in a wild pagan ritual. Although there are no sounds, I can clearly make out the movement of naked bodies as they dance around stone altars. Blazing torches light up the grounds, casting yellowish light on the heavily thatched roofs and stone structures. Forbidding shadows sway to the erotic beat of abandonment and indulgence.

My body breaks into a sweat as nausea strikes my stomach. Something is happening inside the priest's body as well. Suddenly a bolt of horror rips through us and our eyes fill with a blazing fire. Lightning bolts of blue and white rage down from the black sky, vaporizing the entire side of a temple! Bodies are tossed through the air as flesh, bone and rock vaporize into oblivion. Natives scatter in all directions as flames engulf the area. Through the smoke and cinders we see bodies writhing in agony. Some are dying, some are kneeling in terror trying to make amends with the angered Gods. Horror grips me as I feel the anguish my symbiotic priest is feeling. His community has just been destroyed, his world vaporized before his eyes. I feel his grief and loss and something else—there is another sensation deep inside my chest, originating from deep inside his heart—he knew this was going to happen! It's the feeling of remorse and guilt he struggles with that gives him away.

Suddenly a flash of images bursts forth into my mind. He is standing on a high rock and is speaking to a group gathered before him. He warns them that if they continue their irreverent ways, the Gods will punish them. He implores them to abandon their indulgences in the flesh, in the dark forces and in selfishness. He pleads with them to return to their faith and to their worship of the earth and nature and animals. But they do not listen to him. Instead, they banish him from their community. Disheartened, he climbs to a high place away from time, a place where he can ask for guidance and forgiveness for his people. From his perch atop the world, he looks down upon the landscape of denial, searching for just one soul who aspires to truth. There! Far below, in the midst of the rubble and smoke, stands a solitary figure. Although they cannot recognize each other physically, they immediately make a connection. It is *evil* that greets him. With open arms, this darkness does not gloat, but rather conveys assurance and truth.

> Behold this destruction and embrace it well 'my other,' for it is destined to be. The young must learn and the old must endure. The lost must fall and the found must see—that from the beginning of time until the end of space, the forces of creation and destruction will endure. I, the evil, am nothing more than the antithesis of you. Like a mirror image, L I V E / E V I L one gives life to the other and the other validates its creation in the image of its maker. Weep as you must and pray as you will, for you are being true to your nature, and so must I. Let us stand in the truth and no longer lie, that together we'll dance until the end of time.

Closing my eyes, I fall back into the rock alcove. Exhaling forcefully, I feel a strange liberation. Along with his loss, grief and remorse, this priest also feels a sense of peace, even fulfillment. It's as if he heard the message from his evil counterpart and accepted its paradoxical truth. Rather than resist his sadness, he is now able to include it. Not only that, he can even use his grief to forge a more mature part of himself, a part capable of dealing with pain and loss and sorrow. His courage and faith inspire me to commit myself to more maturely embracing the joys, tragedies and passions in my life. Little do I know I'm about to grapple with the depth of my resolve.

A view of the Principal Temple that shows the section of stone terracing that is missing from the hillside.

CHAPTER TEN

SOVEREIGNTY:

THE FIFTH DIMENSION OF KNOWING

Come, into your secret sovereign lair
Like the Puma who pounces there
Stay, with the power of your eternal soul
Like the snake who waits in her earthen hole
Go forth boldly into the spirit we share
Like the Condor who flies in magical air!

The moon continues to shine through high clouds and casts its yellow glow over the summit of Wayna Picchu. I'm ready to step into the burn zone again and, as I lean back into the familiar stone seat, I know the next inspired message is on its way. I open my notepad and steady myself for a flurry of insight.

> *Be alone again in your Sovereignty—that we may be together, you and I. Be simple again, that we may talk of essential things. Make not wants and desires, for in their absence you will truly seek and surely find what has been known by us from the alpha to the omega, what has inspired the mind of God to create and then destroy.*

This time the *Inca Fire* casts me into an exotic series of memories filled with terror, insight and remarkable lessons of *Sovereignty*.

Lush banana trees, deep green ferns and rainbow-colored birds of paradise surround me. The humid tropical air and thick, moist clouds reek with sweet ginger and damp humus earth. Through the dense jungle canopy I catch a glimpse of a sky ablaze with amber, purple and orange hues. The Haiku mountain range shoots up before me like a cluster of gigantic moss-covered stone sabers. I've been hiking since daybreak and haven't encountered a living soul the entire day. Suddenly the idea of venturing into the jungles of Hawaii seems like a bad idea. I pick a spot under a large banana tree to catch my breath and get my bearings. As my backside connects with the damp ground, mild paranoia sets in.

What if I can't find my way back to the car? Or what if I'm attacked by a wild boar? Or what if— "That's enough!" I yell out to myself. "I can't even enjoy the natural beauty around me because I am so scared of who-knows-what." Suddenly a cool tropical breeze nudges me out of my self-disgust and I realize it's time to move on. I stand up and head directly into the light evening breeze. Walking into the breeze is a technique I picked up from reading Carlos Castaneda books. The idea is to act like a "warrior," which includes cupping one's fingers up into one's palms and facing into the breeze each time it changes direction. If it worked for Carlos, who knows, maybe it will work for me. After an hour or so I don't notice any increase in my personal power, but my eyes are so dry from the breeze that I have trouble blinking.

It is the summer of 1973 and I have just moved to Oahu, Hawaii, to surf, party and study behavioral sciences. One of my classes required that I gain some "field experience" in an area I was personally interested in, the relationship between fear and paranoia. To complete the assignment I decided to venture into a remote part of the island called the Haiku Valley. Had I known the kind of experience I was about to gain, I might have dropped the class instead.

As I make my way through the dense jungle, the evening shadows dull the radiant tropical hues. I come to a fork in the narrow dirt path. I have two choices: I can head straight up and over the steep mountain range, or snake downhill into dense jungle. I hesitate for a long time, debating which path to take. "Why can't you just make a decision and stick with it?" I ask myself. "What is the problem here?" The only answer that comes is that I might choose the "wrong" path. It's a valid concern, as my recent track record for making smart choices hasn't been so good. Relationships, friends, school, you name it, I screwed it up. After a few more moments of self-doubt, I come to the conclusion that I'm probably going to mess it up regardless of which path I take, so I shrug my shoulders and trek down into the dense underbrush.

As I move deeper into the jungle, the air cools and the available light dims. The ambiance of a colorful paradise slowly shifts into foreboding shades of gray. The earthen smells of rotted leaves and damp soil now exude an ominous scent. Shadowy figures dart behind suspicious-looking banana leaves and blistered bark. In reaction to an eerie feeling of being watched, I crouch down next to a huge greenish-brown fern. In a frozen stare, I spot a spider's web spun between two leaves of the fern. A small yellow and red spider sits motionless in its center as minute vibrations shake its spindly legs. Fresh dew glistens in silence as it clings to tiny silken threads. The silence is suddenly shattered.

"Tap, tap, tap," rings out through the air.

"What the hell is that," I whisper into my shaking kneecaps.

"Relax, it's probably nothing," I counsel myself.

"Tap tap tap. Tap, tap, tap," rings out again, as the tiny spider impulsively withdraws its spindly legs into the center of its body.

It sounds like bamboo slapping up against a tree trunk. But where is it coming from? Behind me? No. In front? No, not there either. Then my worst fear is realized.

"Ova hee-ahh!" a gruff voice booms out from the dense underbrush.

My legs are like rubber but I somehow manage to turn on my

heels and peer into the direction of the voice. Time collapses in around me as my head roars with unbridled panic.

"Ova hee-ahh!" the male voice blasts again with a thick piercing accent.

"Ova hee-ahh," is a slang phrase the locals in Hawaii use for "over here." My mind races to calculate my survival odds. What is this guy doing way out here in the jungle? I know I have to respond to his call, but I'm numb with fright. Speak up damn it! I bark at myself. I force my clinched jaw open.

"Who are you?" I announce hastily.

"Ne-vah mine that now. You come ova hee-ahh!" he snaps back.

"He's there to my left," I whisper, as I turn to the right and get ready to bolt.

"You can't run and you can't hide, haole," he quips.

I know the word haole. Pronounced *how-lee*, it's slang for "white man without spirit." The name was given to the first European explorers by the Hawaiians because they saw Europeans as unspiritual people, disconnected from themselves and from the divine. Since "breath" is associated with the breath of life, or spirit, the foreigners were dubbed "ones without spirit."

His piercing command causes my knees to weaken. He's right, I'm in *his* territory and there's nowhere to run. My only hope is to try to befriend him. I had learned a survival trick back in grade school that sometimes kept the bullies from pounding on me. The ploy was to try to get on their good side.

"I'm not gonna run. I'm looking for some answers," I reply.

There is a long silence and then a dark figure steps forward into the faint moonlight. He's a small, elderly man, no more than five feet tall. He's thin, but is in unusually good shape. His oily dark hair is riddled with strands of gray and straggles down beyond his collar. He is wearing a tattered green and red short-sleeved cotton shirt and baggy green trousers with a rope belt. Weathered leather sandals are strapped to his bare feet. Although his physical appearance isn't much different from most local islanders, there is something *very* different about him. He has the countenance of a wild animal and moves with unusual agility.

"Lookin' for an-saws? What kine an-saws you lookin' for way out hee-ahh?" he responds, raising his arms from his sides.

"I've come out into the jungle to learn how to deal with self-doubt and fear," I answer with a high degree of paranoia.

The moonlight illuminates the whites of his eyes as he retorts, "You come to da right place bro, cuz theeze is Kahuna land."

I've been in Hawaii long enough to know that a "kahuna" is a Hawaiian witch doctor, the equivalent of a shaman. I also know there is only one remaining kahuna in Hawaii, Sam Lono. Beside being the chief shaman, he is the primary force behind eradicating foreigners from the islands. The term "lono" means "God of fertility and spirit of life." Sam Lono, in addition to keeping the spirit alive for the Hawaiian people, is also notorious for placing curses on land developers, government officials and politicians. According to local people in the community, many of his spells succeed, causing misfortune, sickness, and even death. The man standing before me is revered by many and feared by all.

"You are Sam Lono." I say.

He nods abruptly in agreement, "How you know my name?"

"I've been in the islands only a short time, but I have heard of you often."

"And who ahh you, haole?"

"My name is Val Jon Farris."

"Vol Jon Farce," he repeats with a twang. "What kine name is theeze?"

Before I can answer, he adds, "Vol Jon, I lookin' for sum an-saws too. Like why you trespass on my land? We get some an-saws tonight I tink."

"What do you mean, sir?" I plead.

"You come, stay, go weeth me now." he snaps back, ignoring my question.

"But wait a minute!" I squeal.

He doesn't grab me as I expect, instead he suddenly whips around and takes off down the dimly-lit trail. I'm not sure if it's terror that moves my feet or some bizarre kind of trance, but rather than running away, I lurch forward and follow closely behind him. I can't believe this! Am I losing my mind? Am I under some kind of spell? This is insane. If he kills me, I deserve it.

The drunken, disconnected movement of my body reminds me of running in a dream. I can see my feet kicking forward beneath me, but the act is not fully registering. The scenery around me is a blur as Sam Lono runs ahead of me inside an obscure translucent cloud. I feel strangely calm as I move. It's a feeling of well-being coupled with an intuition that everything will be all right. Our pace slows and we soon come to a stop. To our left, among a grove of banana trees, I see a clearing in the dense jungle. In the middle of the clearing is a small wooden shack with rough vertical timber walls and a palm leaf roof. The dilapidated building has a window without glass and a battered old wooden door with a rope handle. To the right of the shack is a small woodpile with a long-handled axe sticking out of a monkey pod tree stump. To the left, a narrow stream runs through spindly bamboo and young banana trees. As my eyes follow the stream, I come upon a humorous sight. Right in the middle of the creek, dug into the ground, is an old, white, cast iron bathtub. It's clear that it has been intentionally placed there so the water will run in the front and flow out over the back rim. Obviously a natural bathing facility, it makes sense to me at one level, as there is no electricity or city water for miles, but it's a funny sight nonetheless. I turn toward Sam, about to comment, when I notice he is not amused.

"You say you want an-saws 'bout fee-ahh? Why you want theeze?"

"Fear has always bothered me. I need to learn how to trust myself more and not be so afraid of things."

"Ahh you afraid now haole?" he asks, staring into me.

"Yes. Yes, I believe I am."

"Theeze is a strange ting you ahh do-een. Why you come way out hee-ahh onto my land for theeze?"

"I didn't know it was your land. I have always used nature as a way to help me understand things and I thought that spending time in the jungle might help me."

"So you respect nature, yeah? And what 'bout theeze land? Do you respect it too?" he asks, pointing to the clearing.

"I certainly do. I also know that this land belongs to the Hawaiian people and that it was unfairly taken from you. I didn't mean to be disrespectful by coming here. I didn't realize I was trespassing."

My response seems to please him. His face slowly turns from stern to warm, and his eyes begin to sparkle.

"What else you know of like theeze?" he asks, cocking his head slightly.

"What do you mean Mr. Lono?"

"Is okay you call me Sam. What else like theeze tings you know?"

"I know that the Hawaiian people respect the land and consider it sacred. I know that you are an important person to the local people because you stand up for their beliefs and you fight when needed. I also know that your people struggle with trying to save their heritage and keep their customs alive."

"Theeze is good. I tink I will help you with your fee-ahhs. You come, stay, go with me now," he says as he turns and walks toward his shack.

I hesitate for a moment. Trusting him might be a mistake. Besides what is this "come, stay, go" stuff? It sounds strange. He immediately turns around, sensing my hesitation.

"Fee-ahh got you again, huh, haole?" he chides me with a smile.

As I follow him inside, my eyes take a few moments to adjust to the dark. In the middle of the room I see a small round wooden table and three straight-backed chairs sitting unevenly on a dirt floor. In the far corner is an old army cot, a splintered wooden box and an old oil lantern with a soot-stained glass flue. I notice the left wall is covered from floor to ceiling with glass jars filled with herbs, roots and murky liquids. Most of the jars have wax paper lids and are wrapped with twine, while others are sealed with dark wax or claylike substances. "What a place," I whisper to myself. The smell of herbs and dust stings my sinuses. Although the

101

surroundings are alien to me, I take in everything I can, knowing it is a privilege to be here.

Pointing to the wall of jars, he says, "Theeze ahh my sacred medicines. Some heal, some wound and some ee-vahn kill. Theeze one is for you tonight," he adds, as he removes a jar from the top shelf. I can't make out its contents, but I don't get a pleasant feel. My mind races and I begin to panic. Is he going to wound me, heal me or kill with this jar?

"You come, stay, go weeth me tonight Vol Jon," he whispers, gently placing the jar on the table in front of me. As I peer into the container a sickening feeling rushes through my body. He motions me to sit and I reluctantly obey. He then slowly walks to the far corner of the room, picks up the oil lantern and brings it back to the table. He pulls the glass flue off with one hand, strikes a wooden match on the tabletop with the other, and lights the oily wick. Black smoke billows up for a moment and then disappears, leaving an eerie yellow glow in the room. In the lamplight I can better make out the contents of the jar sitting before me. At first, it looks like pickled vegetables or fruit. But as I examine it closer, I see the outline of what looks like a heart! It looks too small for a human heart, but then again, it might be a child's for all I know. My own heart races and my face sears with heat. He grabs my left wrist and pulls my hand toward the jar.

"Time to make da kine fee-ahh come to you so you can leave 'em go," he whispers.

As the flesh on my left hand connects with the cool glass, a chill runs up my arm and into the center of my chest. My heart races and my rib cage shivers in fear.

"Fee-ahh makes the heart go cold," Sam continues.

"What do you mean?" I ask, jerking my hand away from the jar.

Without saying a word, he walks over to the wooden box lying next to the cot, picks up the box and brings it back to the table. He sits down and slowly opens the lid. My worst fear is about to be realized—he *is* going to kill me! He must have a knife in there and he's going to plunge it into my heart! Violent images paralyze me as my breathing halts. The lid comes down and there in his hand is—a scroll? It's a paper scroll, not a knife at all. Sam holds an old weathered document rolled up and tied with a string. Why do I have to make up the worst when I don't know something? Fear makes me worry and blow everything way out of proportion. I've often exhibited this pattern of pessimism.

"Vol Jon, you come stay here in theeze moment weeth me. No more make fantasy," he states sternly.

Now I know a little more about his phrase "come, stay, go." The "come" part has something to do with being present in the moment rather than drifting off into fantasyland. Leaning forward at the table Sam slowly unrolls the old and weathered document and continues, "Theeze document is both sacred and worthless."

"What do you mean sacred and worthless?" I ask, straining my eyes to read the aged text on the scroll.

Flattening the document out on the tabletop, he explains that it's an original land deed signed in 1890 by Queen Lilio'ukalani, a member of the Royal court. The deed proves rightful ownership of a large portion of Hawaiian land, extending from the mountains of Haiku all the way down to the Kaneohe shoreline, which was stolen by European missionaries. As he reads sections of the document out loud, he explains that, because the legal system had become corrupt after the white men invaded their land, the courts would not honor the deed.

"Theeze coldhearted acts of betrayal by da missionaries stem from fee-ahh."

"Fear, not greed?" I ask quizzically.

"Greed comes from fee-ahh. Theeze missionaries lived in fee-ahh cuz they had no connection with 'Mu.' Without Mu, they had no spirit breath. Without theeze, they look foa truth in otha places."

"What is 'Mu,' Sam?" I ask.

Stamping his foot on the ground solidly, he replies, "Mu is da kine ground of spirit. It is da firm heart of nature. Nature is expression of Mu cuz it makes many beautiful tings we can see.

Mu is also da kine connection weeth air and sky, which is breath for spirit." Moving his hands artistically as he speaks, he continues, "Spirit breath, like Mu, is da kine movement of life. Just like we make breathe, spirit breath is in and out, come, stay and go, always mooveen, nevah one ting in pah-teek-yah-lah, but many tings in general."

"And what did you mean when you said the missionaries were looking for answers in other places?"

"Weethout Mu, we lose da connection with spirit and nature, an' listen to otha people foa truth. White man's church geeve 'em truth, called take ow-ahh land an' convert ow-ahh people to believe in theya God. Theeze missionaries believe da church 'truths' and so feel good about steal ow-ahh lands."

His explanation shows me a new way to view fear. How he explains it, it makes sense that fear can fuel greed, theft, and even betrayal. It sheds a different light on why people do some of the rotten things they do, and makes me wonder if the fear in my life is the result of believing others, rather than trusting myself.

"Vol Jon, I tink you lose connection weeth Mu and it makes fee-ahh inside da heart," Sam says, as he presses his right hand against my chest.

My body tightens and the ambient light in the room takes on an eerie otherworldly glow. Like a fast-acting drug hitting my system, time slows to a snail's pace and a tingling giddiness surges through my torso. Shadows cast by the yellowed lamplight transform into a band of drunken gnomes writhing in bliss. Their images then slowly mutate into an ominous mosaic of light and dark patterns that blurs the line between the outer world of certainty and the underworld of chaos and witchery.

"Tell me what is in da heart, Vol Jon," Sam asks pointedly.

Before I can answer his question, images of violence, abuse and terror burst forth in my mind. I begin to recount for him agonizing nights of abandonment and isolation I experienced as a child. I talk of times I felt trapped, misunderstood and judged harshly. Images of wanting to strike out, wanting to fight back but never really doing so fill my mind. Soon a huge lump forms in my throat and my eyes fill with tears.

"You look ova hee-ahh and stay weeth me," he says as he points to his face. Suddenly his face begins to shift and change. His features morph into wild grotesque forms and the edges of his face disperse into the flickering light. "I'm really tripping," I think to myself. There's no clear delineation between Sam's body and everything else in the room. He's literally blending into space before my eyes. The only physical remnants left to adhere to are his blazing coal black eyes. Looking deeply into them, I suddenly realize I'm looking into mirrors—mirrors that display a series of distantly familiar images. I travel deeper into the black swirling reflections, and a surge of fear bolts through my body when I realize what I see.

"Come!" Sam shouts in a gruff voice.

My mind races and urges me to bolt from my chair, but I'm paralyzed. Fear grips me just as it did each time I awoke from a childish nightmare when I was a boy. Again, I stare into the black mirrors, seeing the image of a child being wheeled into a hospital elevator. He's strapped down to a gurney and can't move his arms or legs. His mother is there, waving good-bye to him as the elevator doors close. Looking down on his face I realize that the little boy is me! Terror rips through my numb body. Looking through his eyes, I see white masks and bright lights hovering over me. Buzzing sounds, strange machines and faces loom over my struggling torso. My heart pounds hard against the strap cinched around my heaving chest. A clear plastic mask comes down over my face. I kick and scream and then a sickening sweet smell fills the mask and I fade into oblivion.

The next thing I know, I'm alone lying in a hospital bed with my throat on fire and my head pounding. Looking around frantically I realize there's no one else in the room. I'm alone, scared and hurting badly. I burst into tears and my body shakes violently in disbelief. "Why isn't anybody here with me?" I ask, sobbing. "Why did they do this to me and then leave me?" Thoughts of confusion and panic fill my foggy head. Lying here all alone I conclude they must not love me. No one cares enough to be here with me. My trust in others dies and when it does, so does my trust in myself. Silence fills the moment as my perception shifts out of his tiny shattered life and back into his future persona, the present-time "me." Coming out of the trancelike state, I refocus my eyes on the black mirrors. Slowly they transform from chilling flat surfaces back into Sam's empathic and wise eyes.

"That's when I lost my self-certainty. It's what made me start doubting myself and looking for assurance from others!" I burst out with enthusiasm to Sam.

In retrospect, it was nothing more than a short operation to have my tonsils removed, but to me as a young child it was death, the death of trust in others and in myself. I shake my head violently to disperse the images. When I try to stand, nausea and dizziness grip me. Sam quickly grabs my arm and says, "You *stay* now Vol Jon, and face theeze fee-ahhs cuz there is sum-ting more to see hee-ahh."

My legs go numb as I sink back into the chair. Sam's face returns to normal long enough for me to see his reassuring smile. As I look into his blazing shamanic eyes again, an intense pain suddenly shoots through my head. It's as if a giant claw has grabbed me by the skull! I close my eyes in agony, but Sam nudges me on the chest so I will reopen them. I scream in terror and grip the edges of the table.

"Stay!" Sam yells, as his fist slams down hard on the table.

The oil lamp skitters back and forth, rocking me into an acquiescent lull. The image of an unborn child traveling down the birth canal appears in my mind. The fetus is veiled in darkness, suffocation and fear. A bolt of terror rages up through my legs as I witness the birth process. It's like watching a distant movie scene, but at the same time having all of the intense body sensations that accompany it. Blood smears my vision as a buzzing coldness engulfs me. The baby is coming out feet first. The small, chalky limbs dangle loosely as gloved hands clutch them with alarming force. Intense pain rips down through my body as I struggle for air. This fetus is me! In two worlds now I fight for my life. Blackness and flashes of crimson and blue explode within my tiny soft skull. Here is the real terror, in the first few moments of life. Helplessness and exhaustion paralyze my tender psyche. This tiny unformed mind swims in a sea of symbiotic uncertainty. Hot blood surges through the tangled umbilical cord along with screams of pain and bolts of terror which flow from mother to child. Insane biological messengers cry out in the primal soup of our souls— "Myself, you must now leave me! Out into life you go not as 'us,' but as only 'you.' 'We' must die so that 'you' may live!" Convoluted hot emotion rages into my belly, flooding me with fear and 'seeds' of self-doubt. I've just been rejected, cast out into the coldness of an uncertain world. As incredible as this event sounds, it is as real as anything I have ever experienced in my life.

"Now I remember!" I blurt out to Sam. "My head got stuck and the doctors had to use metal instruments to pry me out." Searing pain explodes in my skull. I'm so terrified I stop breathing in mid-sentence.

"Stay!" Sam demands again.

I know he wants me to stay immersed in the experience, but each time I panic. Again and again I try, confronting only segments of the memory until I finally am able to reexperience the entire event without bolting emotionally. Then, something remarkable happens. I realize that this traumatic separation between my mother and me didn't mean I was unwanted. The fear and pain I experienced through the umbilical cord is probably a natural phenomena that happens to all fetuses. Then I have an astounding insight. What if the "seeds of self-doubt" transferred to me at birth are necessary and are actually planned genetic code used to instill survival within the psyches of the young? It would indeed cast us into fear and self-doubt, but it would also give us the ability to detect danger and defend ourselves. What would happen if I didn't have the emotion of fear? It would be a terrible omission in my emotional make-up. Suddenly something shifts inside me—I no longer see fear as my enemy, but as my ally. In a few moments, the uncontrollable shaking in my body stops, my chest cavity warms and I break into a knowing smile. I sit back in the chair and revel in the lightness present in my body. It's as though a massive weight is lifted from my heart. (Although it sounds incredible that I could remember such an incident, I have no doubt that it happened just as I experienced it. In fact, I later checked with my mother and she verified that I was born breech and that the doctors had to use metal instruments to pry my head out to save my life.)

Now that I have "come" and "stayed" with my worst fears and survived them, I am newly confident. I'm no longer dominated by the presence of fear or self-doubt. They are part of the human condition and I can allow them to be within me without magnifying them. In fact, I now see that they can support me by acting as guides for my ongoing development. Self-doubt can help me to create humility, and fear can assist me in getting out of danger's way. With this newfound awareness, my self-esteem will increase and I can trust myself to know what to do during moments of doubt or fear. As I take a deep breath and exhale in relief, Sam's wise face comes back into view.

"So Vol Jon, it is theeze first fee-ahh at birth that cut you off from Mu."

"Wow! Right out of the chute I was cut off. I'll bet it happens to many children because the birth process can be really intense." I reply.

"Now that you have *come* and *stayed*, you must learn to let *go*," he states, ignoring my revelation.

"Let go? Let go of what?" I ask.

"Of da importance of theeze een-sights. Make no beeg deal 'bout what we have done hee-ahh tonight. It was just time foa theeze unda'standin' in yo-ahh life. Not make self-importance and not make me important, yeah?"

I think I understand what he is saying to me. I should accept what happened without making it a big deal and simply hold it like a gift. I should also let go of thinking that it was a life-altering event as there will probably be many more events in my life that influence me in one way or another. I also think I get the "self-importance" message from him, which basically means to not fall into the trap of becoming a "legend in my own mind."

As I acknowledge Sam's message about letting go, a wave of exhaustion flows through my body and I let my eyes close for a moment . . . as I . . . drift off . . . into a peaceful . . . deep sleep.

When I awaken, I find myself slumped in the same chair I had fallen asleep in the night before. My body feels unusually good for having been draped over a hard wooden chair all night. In fact, I feel better than I have in a long time. It's as if a thousand pounds has been lifted off me. I walk outside and look around for Sam, but he's nowhere in sight. I kneel next to the sunken bathtub and splash cool water on my face. As I gaze at my reflection in the water, I realize that I have been afraid to feel my feelings all my life. In addition, I see how it has always been important for me to be accepted and liked by others. In my reflections, I also realize how defensive and possessive I have been. My main objective has been to make sure that no one ever gets close enough to hurt me or abandon me. But now all that is changed. After having the experience with Sam last night, I'm no longer willing to live my life in fear or self-doubt. I'm going to trust myself and be true to myself from now on. If I like something, I'll say it, and if I don't, I'll say that too. I will risk myself, be vulnerable and share myself honestly and openly with people.

Sam's odd phrase, "come, stay, go" now makes perfect sense. They are the three essential steps for using fear in an empowering way. *Come* close and embrace it, *stay* present with it until the terror subsides, and then when the time is right, let it *go*. As I step away from the bathtub, I realize it's now time for me to go. I look for Sam because I want to thank him for teaching me such profound lessons. I search the clearing, but find no trace of him. Then I think perhaps his absence is a way to help me understand the last of the three steps, letting go. If he were here, I would probably get caught up in what he did for me instead of focusing on what I discovered by confronting my own fears. Assigning credit to another, rather than taking responsibility for my own progress, runs deep. It will take some time for me to let that pattern go, but what better time to begin mastering it than right now?

In silence I walk to the threshold of the long and winding trail that leads back to civilization. I slowly turn to take in the enchantment of Sam's peaceful meadow one last time. It is a divine place, a place of heart and courage and spirit. I will carry this image and my experience of "Mu" everywhere I go. A smile comes to my face as I turn toward the silent jungle. Winding my way uphill, I suddenly catch a glimpse of something rustling in the deep underbrush to my left. Amazingly, my old nemesis, fear, isn't there to dominate me. Instead, I embrace the feeling, stay with it and then let it go. If it's Sam, he already knows I'm grateful, so I don't need to tell him. If on the other hand, it's a predator, well . . . it's gonna miss out on a great meal.

Again the wind whips across the Seat of the Condor, drawing me out of my memory of being with the Kahuna, Sam Lono. The power of *Sovereignty* and being true to myself vibrates within me as two key lessons stand out in my mind. First, being "sovereign" means trusting myself and not allowing fear or self-doubt to dominate me. I am going to take more risks and if I fail, so be it. I'll learn from my failures and use them to strengthen and grow. Second, I am going to be more committed to being true to myself than I am to gaining acceptance from others. In doing this, I will not only gain more respect, I'll also foster meaningful relationships that are based on mature and meaningful values.

CHAPTER ELEVEN

FROM MINI PICCHU TO THE ABYSS

Clutching into space, vivid cries of woe
Away! Away! Ancient faces and dreams of old
Onto her infinite ground I'll now firmly stand
Caught by the vastness of Inca hands
On the horizon of the Andes, gallant clouds do roll
Alone in this moment, I'm finally whole
Alone in this moment, my eternal soul

If I'm going to make the summit by nightfall, I need to move fast. Bowing my head in a moment of silence, I honor the virtual Inca priest who temporarily took up residence inside my body. Straightening my legs, I jump out of the stone alcove and run full-speed up the trail. I stop only to glance back down the mountainside. The coast is still clear, no security guards in sight. Within a few minutes I'm standing on the backside of Mini Picchu. Relief spreads through my body as I drink stale water from my deerskin pouch. Splashing water on my sweaty face, my moment of relief is shattered by the sound of voices. Someone is descending from the trail up ahead. It's unlikely they are tourists. That leaves only one choice—security guards making a last sweep of the site before closing time.

Between the backside of Mini Picchu and the front face of

Wayna Picchu is a short rocky saddle which connects the two mountains. Each side of the narrow ridge drops two thousand feet to the canyons below. The crest of the ridge has a three-foot-wide stone footpath that leads to the steep uphill trail. On the left side of the pathway, a few feet below the surface, I spot a large, fan shaped rock overhang. Under the boulder is a small indentation in the mountain that looks just big enough to hide in. Without a moment's hesitation, I edge my way out over the boulder and slip into the hollow below. Loose rocks and dirt career over the edge and fall into the abyss behind me. I shove my body into the shallow opening as far as it will go, leaving my backside partially exposed. Inch by inch I work my body deeper into the opening until I'm certain that I'm concealed from the trail above.

As my eyes adjust to the darkness, I notice two small green-leafed plants growing out of the soil between the rocks. Each plant has four vibrant leaves and, protruding from their centers, fuzzy green proboscises. I can't help but chuckle to myself as I lay there looking at this tender duo. It looks as if they are sticking their tongues out, chastising me for invading their private sanctuary. What a unique experience. I never would have come across these two chlorophyll characters if I hadn't climbed under this ledge. They sprouted here, will live here and die here, without anyone but me ever seeing them. It reminds me of the Inca families I saw from the train in the agricultural highlands. Like these two little plants, they came forth from the richness and grace of the earth, stretched their roots into the soil, gathered sustenance, sunlight and water and, in a moment of surrender, will return to the same earth that bore them. There are so many secret lives in the world that we never get to see. Wouldn't it be grand to be able to get a glimpse of *every* secret life? Maybe if we were less self-absorbed, we could extend our range of perception to tap into all the hidden lives that exist in the world.

The voices and footsteps approach rapidly. I don't dare move a muscle for fear of being spotted. As I listen intently, I hear the static crackle and squeal of a two-way radio as one of the hikers converses in Spanish. There's no question about it. They *are* security guards. Footsteps muted by dirt and stone pound in my ears as I hear them cross directly above me, and then tread across the saddle to climb over the ridge of Mini Picchu. After waiting a few minutes, I carefully back out of the alcove and grab the rock ledge above my head. Pulling myself up, I fling my right leg up and over the stone and catapult myself back onto the trail.

I'm finally clear of the security guards. I can relax a bit now and plan my ascent route to the summit. As I approach the mountainous edge of Wayna Picchu, I trace the steep footpath winding its way up the sheer rock face. The western slope, which I am now on, is composed of massive, near-vertical shards of gray and white granite that plunge down into the valley far below. Overlapping layers of earth and stone create thin ridges and narrow ledges that the Inca trailblazers used to carve out their intricate pathways. As I carefully study the route, it becomes clear why this part of the ruins is off-limits. The rains have washed out parts of the trail, turning already thin and dangerous ledges into near-vertical suicide. Studying the worst sections closely, I get the sinking feeling that I am about to be challenged *beyond* my abilities.

It's now a quarter after four and the sun is beginning to fade. At most there is one, maybe two, hours of daylight left. I pull my bandanna from my belt, tie back my hair and begin my ascent. In many places along the way the Inca had carved steps right into the rock. In other places they had meticulously wedged pre-carved rectangular stone steps into the ground. The edges of each piece of stone are cut perfectly straight and clean. Like stairways to the Gods, the ancient steps rise straight up into the heavens.

Stopping to catch my breath, I lean back against the near vertical wall and survey the terrain ahead. Above me about thirty feet and out on the edge of a precipice, I notice a ten-foot by ten-foot curved wall of rectangular stones built into the mountainside. In the center of the ancient wall is what appears to be a horizontally protruding piece of stone shaped like a half ring. Upon closer examination the stone ring contains a hole about three inches in diameter. A foot below the ring is a natural indentation in the rock. After studying it, I surmise the indentation was caused by something being inserted down through the ring and wedged into place. A flash of imagination comes to me and I see the image of an ancient wooden torch held solidly within the ring. The torch is ablaze, casting a flickering yellow light and corresponding shadows on the ancient stone face of the earth. A fleeting image of priests and seers climbing this very same route flashes in my head. Their eerie shadows flicker and dance in the torch light as they silently climb to the heavens.

Slowly pressing on, the vertical ascent begins to exhaust my leg muscles. Using my hands as pistons, I push down firmly on my thighs to assist each upward stride. Although it helps, I begin to lose control of the exact placement of my feet. Stumbling and almost losing my balance, my boot slips over the edge of a stone step and dangles into sheer space. Catching myself with my left hand, I regain my balance.

"You can't afford to do that." I tell myself. "Don't take a single step without absolute certainty."

To complicate matters, I soon come upon one of the washed out areas of the trail. As I study the terrain closely, I shake my head slowly in disbelief. To my left, no more than a foot or so away, the edge of the trail falls away. To my right, a sheer wall shoots straight up into the sky. Directly in front of me and on an eighty-degree incline, the stone steps vanish into a washed-out mass of loose rocks and damp earth. The washout extends for about ten feet across the face of the mountain before it reforms into a solid trail. On the far side of the washout a switchback rises straight up and then cuts back sharply to the right above me. Fortunately the damaged section contains stone protrusions and vegetation that may serve as handholds. If I intend to survive this challenge, my approach must be extremely well thought-out.

There, then there, then . . . no, that won't work. Okay, let's try again. Right hand there, left foot there, left hand there, then follow with the right foot and edge your way across. Okay, that should do it. Now, one more important thing . . . whatever you do, don't look down.

Gripping a pointed rock that protrudes from the mountainside with my right hand, I edge my left foot out onto the thin, loose ledge. I assess its firmness before putting my full weight down. Satisfied, I press down hard and stretch my left arm way out to grab a clump of roots growing from the earthen wall. Following with my right foot, I wedge it closely next to my left foot. Shifting my weight, I lift my left foot again and move it further out into the washout. Finding a small foothold, I jam the tip of my boot in as far as it will go. Cautiously, I place my weight on it to check its strength.

Oops! My boot slips a few inches into soft soil. Sweat runs down my chilled back as my left hand instinctively clutches the bundle of plant roots. I stall for a moment, check my reflexes and loosen my jaw. My legs shake fiercely as I take a deep breath and close my eyes to center myself. The afternoon wind dances on my face, teasing my mortality. How gripping the threat of death can be. The impulse to survive lingers behind such a thin veil of sanity. To avoid panic, I use a trick I learned during a previous expedition. It doesn't come naturally, but if I really focus and breathe *into* the fear and stay with it rather than avoid it, a subtle calm begins to surface. It doesn't replace the terror, but the calm helps balance it. The results are objectivity and assurance, which in this moment are in short supply.

"All right, now, pay close attention. Just stay cool and rely on your senses," I counsel myself. If there's any time to rely on myself, this is it. A split second's worth of self-doubt could cost me my life. I slowly shift my weight back to my right foot and search for a firmer toehold on the washed-out terrain. Then I make a terrible mistake. Violating my most important rule, I accidentally catch a glimpse of the abyss between my legs.

Gut-wrenching terror rips through my body as I lose my balance.

An example of the sheer cliff trails built by the Inca to reach the high summits of Machu Picchu.

CHAPTER TWELVE

FAITH:

THE SIXTH DIMENSION OF KNOWING

Mystical horizon, this invisible you
Drawing me near, I lose my ground
My ears are buzzing with unsounding sound
A Free fall of faith engulfs me with glee
To thy place where ancient souls run free
The end of this waiting, the beginning of me
Moving into the curve, moving into the curve
Moving into the curve of eternity

Ancient Inca faces glimmer and glow within the *Inca Fire* as I prepare myself for traveling into the next dimension of knowing. What's going to happen in the fiery burn zone this time? Where in my past will it lead me? The answer comes swiftly:

Look not for what you will never see—for your eyes deceive your senses and your senses fool your mind. Instead, climb to a high place away from time. Make simple your mind and open your heart to Faith. Then touch the earthstone of eternity and the Light of the Masters will come to you and illuminate the way.

A panorama of pure blackness bursts forth through the flames drawing me into its virtual abyss. Memories pour out of my mind and into the void, transporting me into the infinite arms of *Faith*.

As I approach the bridge railing, the strong breeze billowing from the valley floor presses hard against my face. I move toward the edge and catch a dizzying glimpse of the ravine far below. The full moon highlights the rocky crags and turbulent river 180 feet below. No normal right-minded individual would consider hurling their body into this abyss. But then again, I'm not your normal right-minded individual.

It is fall of 1992 and I had just finished leading a weekend self-development workshop, when a friend called and asked if I'd like to do a bungee jump. A group of paratroopers were getting together that night to try out some new equipment and needed a few people to test the setup. The idea of jumping off a bridge in the dark was intriguing, but being a guinea pig for *new* equipment somehow added an extra element of terror to the invitation. Such an opportunity could either open new possibilities for me or kill me. With some trepidation, I accepted my friend's invitation and we agreed to meet at midnight near the Rubicon River bridge located in the Sierra Foothills. As I drive to the site, I question my sanity.

"Are you crazy? Why would you risk your life doing something like this? There's a reason this came up, so don't fight it. Well, if someone invited you to commit suicide, would you do it just because it came up?"

Bungee jumping isn't a hare-brained death wish on my part. Extreme rituals such as this have been used for centuries as spiritual rites of passage. In its earliest form, bungee jumping was called "vine jumping." Originating on a small South Pacific Island in the New Hebrides chain of Melanesia, the islanders vine jumped for spiritual guidance and to settle domestic and community disputes. Before the ceremony, natives built elaborate, eighty-three-foot towers out of sticks, logs and vines. Willing tribe members then climbed to the top of the precarious structures and tied seventy-five-foot-long vines to their ankles. In a moment of heightened prayer, clasping their hands to their chests, they leaped off into space. Their velocity increased exponentially as they plunged toward the ground. Then, if all went well, at the last moment, the vines stretched tight and stopped them from smashing headfirst into the earth.

Not only have native tribes used such terrorizing rituals to deepen their spiritual understanding, but more civilized societies have also participated in similar activities. The Greek philosophers called these ritualistic activities acts of "transmigration." Transmigration was a main object of study for Plato and Pythagoras, and was a cardinal feature in the development of Hinduism, Buddhism and the Jewish Kabbalah. This "migration" is basically the act of moving one's identity out of the familiar, yet cramped house of the ego, into the vast real estate of the soul. Most Third World shamanistic activities also include some form of transmigration to evoke spiritual faith and physical healing.

Although there are libraries filled with theological texts and religious disciplines, many, in my opinion, are steeped in jargon, dogma or metaphysical mumbo jumbo. This ritual has some teeth in it because it requires a real leap of faith. Technically, the leap is meant to cause the demise of the identity and, more specifically, to break one's attachment to survival. The trick is obviously to release the attachment without losing the life.

"Who's going to jump first?" Our jumpmaster asks with a twinkle in his eye.

I wait for the courageous or stupid to volunteer, but no one responds, so I step forward. "I will," blurts from my rebellious lips.

"All right, step up to the railing so we can hook you in, Val Jon," he says, guiding me closer to the edge.

"On this side of the rail or on that side?" I ask meekly, as I step up to the railing. "This is insane," I whisper, as he secures the bungee cord to my snug body harness.

"Now move your leg out over the railing."

In one terrifying motion, I swing my right leg over the padded rail and straddle it like a celestial cowboy about to meet his match. This is what I said I wanted—an experience that would teach me something about faith. Well, I am certainly tapped to the max in this moment.

"What? Huh? Can you repeat the instruction please?" I ask.

"Sure," he laughs. "Swing your other leg outside the railing and step down below that overhang. There's a support beam about two feet below that you can stand on."

"Is losing my life worth this research?" I whisper to myself as I dangle precariously far above the ravine.

"Okay, now turn around and face out into the canyon," he directs me.

Don't panic, cool it, here's your chance to get some firsthand data. "I don't care about data," screams inside my head as I wrench my torso toward the gaping abyss.

To complete the move, I have to extend my arms up over my head, and then fold them over the padded railing behind my pounding skull. What a sight I must be! My chest extends up toward the sky, forming the illusion of fearlessness. It's clear to me that tapping into this terror demands complete surrender. Although many people bungee jump for fun, I'm interested in accessing something more substantive, something that will teach me about faith and surrender. To take this leap of faith, I must release my grip on my history, dreams, hopes, plans, my identity, my life itself. To let go of the railing behind me, I must deny my survival instincts. I must ignore my ironclad willfulness, the one that always got me through things in the past. Now I'm having a firsthand experience of the dominating power of fear and the primal drive to survive. Terror and unchecked willfulness permeate every cell in my body. This experiment is fast becoming a real bad idea. Suddenly I don't trust this setup. The bungee cord looks too thin, the harness is too loose. I'm the first jumper and the gear might fail. The jumpmaster is younger than me, so how can he be trusted? My mind races out of control. These are valid concerns, damn it. I'm not just making this stuff up. People have died in situations like this.

"Pick a spot on the horizon and when you're ready, jump!" someone shouts from behind my pounding skull.

The panorama of mountains and sky dizzies me. I lose my equilibrium and impulsively clutch the padded rail behind me. Now I know the real purpose of the padding—it's to prevent bloody fingertips.

"Hold on a minute! I—I'm not ready yet!" I yell back.

I'm now face to face with losing my identity and *it* isn't pleased about it. My need for control and safety grabs me and shakes me violently. No one is gonna make me jump from this damn bridge until *I'm* ready! I've dealt with fear in the past and I know from experience that I need to embrace it, but this is way beyond fear. This is a raging terror ripping through every cell in my body.

"Embrace it." I think to myself, but no matter how hard I try it's just too intense. Images rush in my head of all the times I've escaped harm due to my willfulness. I have prided myself on my ability to handle threatening situations, but this time my willfulness is powerless. Oh, sure I can force myself to jump, but that isn't the same as letting go. Standing on the cold steel structure I realize I'll need to surrender completely if I want to experience even a flicker of faith. Then I have another insight. I can never *will* my way through this experience. I can't do here what I have always done in the past. In fact, not only can't I make myself ready, it's not even *my* decision to make. The drive to hold on to *my* intention, *my* abilities, even *my* willingness, is getting in the way of surrender.

Not only do I need to let go of holding on, I also need to let go of letting go. Letting go in this terrifying moment seems an impossible task. I'm powerless to act in *any* way that will further the process. It's hopeless. Hopelessness is something I've avoided my whole life. I have always refused to hit bottom. I resisted giving up on anything. It was against my nature, unthinkable, unbecoming. What I had never realized before was that, until I allow myself to experience hopelessness, I can't possibly surrender. And without surrender, faith is unattainable. All right, it's hopeless. There is nothing I can do here. My mental chatter stops and my heart pangs deep in my chest. The acceptance of hopelessness, although depressing, shifts my perception. I'm no longer frozen by the terror. It's now moving within me like transitory enthusiasm, similar to walking on one of those horizontal "people movers" at an airport. I pop out of depression and am swept along toward willingness and openness. In a moment of pure surrender, my body relaxes. The only thing that holds me up is the bungee cord lying across the padded railing. In an extended moment of silence and peace I find myself whispering the words, "I surrender."

The sky rests on the gentle curve of the earth. I hear my blood flow past my swollen ear canals—or maybe it's the river rapids rushing far below. As the wind caresses my pinched face, I relax further and allow myself to breathe. Looking down into the abyss, my shoe tips serve as leather gun sites pointing the way to oblivion. The distant river below looks like a piece of white thread cast down by the Gods. And the Gods, in this moment, demand unconditional surrender, something I have avoided my whole life. I fill my lungs beyond capacity, my nostrils flare, and without another willful thought, I let go and leap into the void!

Falling head over heels, my identity bursts into a million splinters, each piece vying desperately to anchor with a railing, but dying before it can adhere. My identity shatters, and as it does, something happens to the "me" I have come to know so well. Incommensurable and beyond language, there is, in this eternal moment, no "me" left. No ego, no self, no history, no past. Unfathomable to the mind, this is an experience of unity beyond all comprehension. I'm not in shock or unconscious though, because I am fully aware as my body hurtles toward the river rocks below. I'm not dissociating either, I'm fully conscious of everything that's happening. What's incredible is that the fall *is* being experienced, but I can't tell *where* it's being experienced from. There is no reference point from which to view the activity. I'm witnessing my fall from an invisible, surround sound perch, similar to listening to music with headphones on and not being able to pinpoint exactly where the tunes are coming from.

From somewhere outside my body, I witness the river below exponentially growing in size and I can see my body twisting and flailing like a rag doll in the wind. Then the images fade as the harness tightens around my chest and the bungee cord grows taut. I observe my body catapulting straight back up into the air. As it hurls toward the underside of the bridge, "I" snap back into its limp frame. Terror grips every molecule of my body. I'm going to hit! But incredibly, rather than put my arms up as protection, I let them relax. It's so unusual to be willing to die while thinking about death. It's like having a wise old mentor listen to the immature child inside of me have a tantrum.

I don't hit the bridge, but I do bounce up and down four or five times. When I finally come to a standstill, my identity reintegrates itself into my traumatized body. "I" am back, but something is very different. "I" am no longer the most important thing hanging around in life. In fact, I now see myself as a minuscule part of a much greater picture. I now have the ability to "witness" my life. Although I'm still feeling everything, part of me is no longer affected by what I'm feeling. It's as if another "me" has come into existence, a me that isn't limited to my history, patterns, limitations, fears, hopes or aspirations. A me that is broad and wide, vast in its capacity.

As I dangle at the end of the bungee cord, I am reminded of a saying from the Indian guru Meher Baba that I had never fully understood until now. The quotation is from his book, *Life at its Best*:

> It does not require a large eye to see a large mountain. The reason is that, though the eye is small, the soul which sees through it is greater and vaster than all the things which it perceives. In fact, it is so great that it includes all objects, however large or numerous, within itself. For it is not so much that you are within the cosmos as that the cosmos is within you.

As the jump team hoists me up, my familiar feeling of fear is now accompanied by a strange and wonderful sense of faith. With each pull on the bungee cord, the vastness of the soul and the power of faith are becoming more present and more real for me. Part of me knows everything is going to be just fine, and "just fine" could include falling to my death before these people can hoist me back over the bridge railing. Twenty feet to go, eighteen, sixteen, fourteen. I can hear them now as they pull me up to the padded railing.

"Well, Val Jon, was that the ride of your life or what?" someone asks. I have no words so I don't answer.

"He's speechless!" he announces in a high-pitched voice to the crowd.

Everyone laughs as they grab me by the shoulders and drag me over the piece of carpet taped to the steel bridge railing. Silently I gaze into their faces, their eyes and their souls. Speechless, I walk to the far side of the bridge and sit on the cold black asphalt. As I stare into a crack in the blacktop, images of family members, friends and partners flood my thoughts. I feel an incredible love and connection with every one of them. Tears fill my eyes as I touch my hands together, overlapping my fingers like I did when I was a child, before saying prayers.

For many years I have known about the concept of faith. But to experience it directly is beyond words. I inhale deeply, letting a wave of warmth fill me. Each breath I take is like my first. The night air fills my lungs and each exhalation feels like it's my last. I am willing to let go and have faith in the procession of life. What an incredible experience—in one moment inspired by a new breath, a new life, and in the next moment, willing to let that inspiration expire, wane and die. My legs shake violently from the residual terror as I reflect on what I had just done. Sitting here, alone on the bridge, I am left with the paradoxical experience of having lost myself and found myself in the same moment.

As my memory wanes, I rub my eyes and hold onto my shaking body. This is an intense lesson for me. I reach down and touch the stone next to the Condor's Seat to ground myself. The dimension of *Faith* resonates within me like a timeless spiritual chant, *"climb to a high place away from time. Make simple your mind and open your heart."* I see from this passage that faith exists beyond the scope of belief. When I have faith, I do not need to believe.

Faith brings a special transcendental quality to the other dimensions of *Humility*, *Eternality*, *Truth*, *Passion* and *Sovereignty*. When *Faith* is present, I need not worry whether I am staying aware of the other five. Faith says, "trust the process and know that even though you may not be aware of any of the other dimensions, they are present inside you and so will illuminate the way for you." What a relief. I was beginning to wonder if I had to become a walking library filled with inspired messages and cryptic prose.

A view of the two thatched roof buildings that sit just in front of the guard shack.

CHAPTER THIRTEEN

FROM THE ABYSS TO THE SUMMIT

Ancient Masters of Inca grace
Pluck my mind from this time and space
Deliver my soul to your mystical fires
And free me of these willful desires!

Reeling back toward the abyss, I scramble to reclaim my balance. I jerk hard on the bundle of roots to stabilize myself, but they rip loose from the mountain. My right hand impulsively grips the stone protrusion as my torso rotates left and out toward the valley. Pressing down hard with my left foot, I counter the movement and slowly bring my body back around to face the washout. My rapid breathing bounces off the cold stone in front of my face, validating that I am still alive.

I search the vertical landscape for a more reliable anchor for my left hand. Just to the left, and a bit higher than where the bundle of roots was, I spot a small granite outcropping. Stretching out, I grip it firmly with my fingertips, extend my left leg again and thrust my boot deep into the loose soil indentation. This time it holds. I slowly scale across the washout until I reach the far side. As I step onto the two-foot-wide trail, relief washes through my tense body. With my feet firmly on solid ground, I look out over the Andes, thankful for the privilege of being alive. Nature is a strange and paradoxical thing. It is beautiful, inspiring and nurturing, and yet it can just as easily terrorize or kill without hesitation.

The green metal cable attached to the rock wall just above my head is a welcome sight. Someone had placed it there to assist climbers up the steep switchback. Pulling myself up, I swing around to my right and land firmly on the steep ascending stone trail. The narrow pathway snakes its way up the western face of the mountainside, curving gently to the left and disappearing into the distance. As I climb, my leg muscles burn from exertion and my lungs sear with pain. Although this is not the highest summit I have climbed, the combination of steep terrain and almost losing my life on the washout takes a toll on my energy level. I slow almost to a crawl and bend over to catch my breath. At this pace I'll never make it to the top by sunset.

"Come on, Val Jon. You can do it. Don't stop now," I urge myself on.

Physical challenges force me to stretch and push myself beyond my comfort zone. As I bend over, I reach inside myself for more energy, more commitment. There is no more energy to be found but the commitment is there. Although my limbs are weak, somehow the commitment empowers them to continue—and somehow they are able to comply. How strange that, in one moment I am convinced I can go no further and, in the next I am able to move on with nothing more than commitment. My "second wind" leads me to question the notion of physical limitations.

The sun now sets over the western ridge of the Andes and the available light quickly vanishes. Parts of the terrain become shadowed and obscure and I have trouble discerning the trail from the edge of the cliff. Staying as close to the mountain side of the path as I can, I trudge my way up the steep, winding footpath. As I approach the base of the summit, ancient stone walls come into view. All around me are ancient altars and ornate cliff reinforcements. What incredible skill and artistic talent the Inca people had. Some of the rock reinforcements jut way out over the vertical cliffs, hanging in free space. It's uncanny how the builders were able to place huge stones in perfect rows on such treacherous terrain. As I advance, I take in every structure, every landmark. This is definitely a sacred place and must have been used by the Inca for high ceremonies. An eerie feeling fills me as my eyes dart around the rubble-laden ruins. The wind wisps across cold, lifeless stone and dark gray clouds fill the sky like vaporous warriors charging into battle. To my left and higher up on the ridge a cluster of huge boulders juts out over the front edge of the summit. The setting sun's rays stream over the top of them, casting ribbons of golden light into open space.

The path curves sharply to the left as it follows the landscape around to the south. The higher I climb, the tighter the curves in the trail become. Spiraling up until I can almost touch the clouds, the path widens out into a pad, similar to a stage, with a massive drape of vertical stone behind it. Standing in this natural theater of the soul, this humble actor silently gazes out into the expansive Peruvian landscape. The curve of the earth reminds me that I am not only seeing a vast mountain range, but an expansive sector of the planet—a planet that is merely a tiny celestial dirtball, flying around a blazing fireball which itself orbits within a spiral galaxy drifting through space. No wonder I seek security and assurance in my life.

When I turn to continue on my journey I discover there is no more trail to follow. I search the small clearing, but there is no sign of a path. I scrutinize the rock wall, thinking there may be an ascent route up its face, but there's no handhold or foothold to be found.

"Okay. Where did I go wrong? I must have missed a turn somewhere. I've climbed all this way to get here, so what do I do now?"

I stand dumbfounded. The right edge of the terrain extends to the edge of the cliff that drops off to the Urubamba Valley. To the left, it merges into an even higher spire of granite that shoots straight up toward the summit. There doesn't seem to be a way around or a way up. Double-checking, I walk to the far left end of the rock wall and examine the area closely. No sign of a trail. I move as far to the right as I can without falling into the gorge, but again, no trace of an ascent route.

"How can this be? The Inca engineers wouldn't build a trail that ended short of the summit. It just doesn't make sense."

I backtrack down the footpath to see if I missed a turn, but find nothing, so I return to the clearing to search more intensely for a clue. Baffled and frustrated, I spot a large flat-topped rock and sit down to assess the situation. Looking out over the valley to the south, I see Machu Picchu far below. Its roofless dwellings and magnificent temples glow in the dim evening light. As I scrutinize the maze of stonework and terraces, I spot a few people still walking around in the ruins. What a grand civilization it must have been. Centuries have passed, yet the grounds seem so alive and vibrant. As I view the agricultural terraces carved into the mountainside, I imagine them filled with exotic plants and vegetables. I picture farmers, like the ones I had seen from the train outside Cusco, cultivating the soil and reaping crops. Moving my gaze back to the temples and altars near the Central Plaza, I visualize ceremonies and rituals that must have taken place there long ago. Wind caresses my face, a wind that may have also caressed their faces.

Perhaps I should stop worrying about finding the way to the top and have a little faith. Let the wind guide me, or my senses, or anything other than my head. In a few moments I am walking again to the right side of the clearing. There, just to the left of an ancient stone doorway, I spot a small opening in the hillside. Examining it more closely I realize it's a cave entrance. I quickly climb up to it and tuck my arms to my sides, poke my head in, and work my body through the narrow opening. My face immediately cools as I inhale the damp fragrance of earth and stone. Scanning the interior of the cave with my flashlight, I estimate its size to be five feet tall, five feet wide, and about twelve feet from front to back.

"This is remarkable. Look at the stone formations in here." My words are rapidly consumed by the dead silence within the secret chamber.

Investigating the ceiling, I spot what looks like a cross between natural rock formations and Inca engineering. On the right side of the ceiling it appears that perfectly shaped rectangular blocks were used to reinforce a natural fault line in the cave's roof. The crafted blocks seem to blend with the area so well I can't tell where Mother Nature stopped and Inca builders began. The upper left section of ceiling is smooth and looks as if it was formed by a huge air pocket that got trapped as molten rock cooled eons ago. I crawl on my hands and knees, deeper into the cave. Although this is a remarkable find, I don't know how it will solve my problem of getting to the summit. Then, just as I'm about to back out, I notice a slender ray of light. Moving closer, I realize I'm not in a cave at all. The "cave" is actually a long narrow tunnel. How ingenious the Inca engineers were to create such a sly diversion. This ploy would definitely confuse intruders and deter them from reaching the summit. Working my way through the narrow damp tunnel, I methodically climb toward the light. The angle of ascent increases until I'm climbing almost vertically. Fortunately, the Incas carved small indentations in the tunnel floor for traction. Finally I crawl out of the stone labyrinth into an open area near the base of the three huge boulders that crown the summit of Wayna Picchu. Making my way up a short trail and through an enclave created by the boulders, I find myself standing in a small area between them. Enthusiasm fills my chest as I realize I'm only a few feet away from the summit.

The ancient stone doorway near the secret tunnel that leads to the Wayna Picchu summit.

CHAPTER FOURTEEN

SERVICE:

THE SEVENTH DIMENSION OF KNOWING

This candle, this life, firm and tall
and round it stands in the darkness
awaiting its turn at a blaze
Let it be ignited and scorched
burned to its ends, that it may cast
every last ray of light against
dim veils and dark walls
Let these paraffin hopes and dreams
vaporize in its flickering heat
not a drop of wax to remain
Leave not a single trace, not a single trace,
of this candle, this life

Dark storm clouds now blanket the entire sky. A chill runs through my body as I slide out of the Seat of the Condor and walk to the northern side of the massive flat boulder. Faint steel blue silhouettes of the Andes blend in with the darkness of night. The wind streams over my face, delivering the cool scent of rock and earth. I'm standing on the top of the world and if I die tonight I'm fulfilled, whole and wanting for nothing. Smiling gently

I return to my ethereal perch and ready myself for the final dimension of knowing. Before I can take my seat these words flow like a sacred river into my mind:

> *The Service of the Master's Light exists beyond the mind and senses and outside of time—in a flash of revelation we suddenly see what we have been blind to all our lives. Has not light been shed on what we were to see all along? What illumination then serves us and enables us to see? The Light of the Masters is not outside to behold, nor is it inside to touch. It is on no side but rather—in the whole of things.*

Translucent flames of gold and red flicker wildly. Intense ribbons of light merge together and then break apart, symbolizing the struggle between unity and separation. As I step forward into the burn zone, the wild flames consume my entire body. A kaleidoscope of images and memories come forth, casting me into a swirling tunnel of white light and into the heart of *Service*.

"Is she yours?" The nurses ask me in unison as they look cockily at each other.

"Grace Oldham?" I ask.

"Yes, she's in room 303 at the end of the hall."

My heart pounds as I walk down the stark white hospital hallway. As I approach her room, I know this is the last time I will see my grandmother alive. Although she's ninety-three, she isn't dying of old age. Three days earlier my grandparents had been taking their daily walk to the shopping mall to have lunch, when a car backed out of a driveway and accidentally ran both of them down. My grandfather was killed instantly and my grandmother was rushed to an intensive care unit. The year is 1986. I was working in nearby San Jose when my cousin called to give me the grave news. Hesitating just outside her room, I now realize why the nurses were acting so oddly. Although the door is closed, I can hear her yelling at the top of her lungs. I panic and bolt through the door. As I enter, the volume of her cries blasts me. There, in a slightly raised hospital bed my grandmother's frail body writhes furiously. She slams her fists against the chrome bed railings, and the plastic tubes attached to her body jiggle wildly. Her fists are clenched so tightly, the sterile overhead light reflects off their mirrorlike flesh.

"Grandma! What's the matter?"

There is no recognition or response, so I bend over closer to get her attention. The smell of rubbing alcohol and urine stings my nose as I yell into her ear.

"It's your grandson Val Jon. Can you hear me, Grandma?"

Her hearing is bad and the cataracts on both her eyes all but blind her, so I've got to do something else to get her attention. I lean in even further, kiss her on the cheek and place my face close to her right ear. Tears come to my eyes as memories flood in of the many years we spent together. Caught in a moment of grief, I remember the times all of us kids sat at her feet and listened to the inspiring stories of her youth. She often recounted for us the dangerous pilgrimage her mother took crossing the country in a covered wagon in the 1860s. She kept us spellbound with remarkable stories of living at the turn of the century and how she and her family survived the depression. But most of all, she filled our hearts with a special kind of unconditional love, a love that only a grandmother can provide. My childhood visions of being with this powerful matriarch slowly fade as I witness before me a frail and vulnerable woman.

"Granny, it's me, Val Jon. I'm here to see how you are doing."

"Leave me alone! I just want to die!" She wails back at me.

"No, Granny, please don't say that. I want you to live. I love you."

Turning away from me sharply, she nearly jerks loose the intravenous tube attached to her right wrist. She wants nothing to do with my pleas and isn't the slightest bit interested in what I want, even if it is in her best interest. I realize that if I'm going to make a connection with her, it must be on her terms. I move back away from her and close my eyes for a few moments to reconsider my approach.

"All right, I understand. I want you to know I love you very much and it hurts to see you suffer like this," I reply respectfully.

After a few moments of silence she rolls over and peers up at me. "Val? Is that you, Val?"

"Yes, Granny! It's me. I'm so worried about you. I want you to get better."

"I don't want to get better!" she snaps.

"But why, Grandma? Why don't you want to get better?"

"I have nothing to live for. I'm alone now. My husband is dead and I'm here by myself. I want to be with him," she says in an agonized tone.

"But there is a lot to live for Grandma. You *aren't* alone."

"No! You don't understand. Stop telling me that!" She bolts away from me again.

"Grandma, you sound so mad. Why are you angry?"

"I've been laying here for three days waiting for God to take me, and he hasn't come for me yet. I'm mad as hell! He took your Grandpa, but left me here all alone!" she blurts out, slamming her fists against the chrome bed railing again.

"Grandma. God will take you when God is ready, not when *you* are," I reply respectfully.

"Don't you speak to me that way!" she rips back, squinting hard at me.

"I'm sorry, Grandma. I didn't mean—"

"—I've suffered my whole life raising my kids." she says, cutting me off. "None of them appreciated me. After all I've done for them, all I've given them, they turned their backs on me, ruined their lives and made everyone around them suffer, including me."

"Grandma, you did the best you could," I console her.

She then takes an illogical turn and says, "Don't you try and make me believe that! It's a lie! I was an *awful* mother to my children. That's why they abandoned me. I should have given them more love. I could have protected them more from their father's rage. I ought to have been stricter with them. If I had cared more they would've turned out better. They would've been happier."

I then realize something very important about our conversation. Every time I try to convince her of something I believe is true, she reacts violently. If I continue to push her, I will lose our rapport altogether. Besides, why am I really here? To serve myself, my own needs and feelings, or am I here for her? I've got to set aside my own fears and concerns and stop trying to change her mind. Even though I love her and want her to get better, the truth is, if she dies, *I'll* be sad. If she leaves, *I'll* feel the loss. Where will *I* turn for the special kind of love and affection she has always given me? I now see that I've been concerned about my needs, not hers. She's ninety-three years old, has a pacemaker in her heart, can barely see or hear, has internal bleeding, twelve broken bones and has just lost her lifelong mate. Never mind *my* needs, what does *she* have to live for at this point? Suddenly it doesn't make a lot of sense to me why she would want to live. If I were in her position, what would I want? Probably the very thing she keeps asking for: to be left alone to die in peace.

Looking blindly up in my direction she continues. "My kids wouldn't listen to me. I tried so hard to be a good mother, but I failed. I did everything wrong. They have suffered horribly because of me and now God is punishing me."

Now is my chance to be here for her, to listen, to serve. It hurts me to see her this way. I want to tell her that her kids made their own choices and that it wasn't her fault, but I know she will resist it. I reach out to hold her frail shaking hand, and she continues. First she talks about Aunt Lota, an alcoholic who died of emphysema, liver failure and cancer. Next, Aunt Donna, who for years was entombed in a body riddled with rheumatoid arthritis before passing away. And then there was Uncle Elmo, who suffered with lymphoma for five years before it killed him. She saves my father for last, her only remaining living child. She tells me he had been terrorized, beaten and abused by his father, and how he would come to her in the middle of the night and sob in her arms. Tears fill my eyes again as I realize why my father had been so violent and unpredictable with me. It was a learned behavior and, like a diabolical legacy, rage cascaded down through the generations from father to son.

Waves of emotion wash over me as I listen to her painful reflections. I indulge in my own feelings as I listen. For years I held anger and hurt over the abuses that occurred in my own childhood. With each breath I take, the grip of self-indulgence tugs on me. I know I must be here for her and allow her to express her anguish, yet I am hurting, too. Caught up in two worlds, I struggle to keep them from collapsing into a firestorm of self-pity and collusion. My struggle is deepened because of my desire to take away her pain and suffering. I can't bear to witness her agony, yet I'm helpless to alleviate it. I can't take it away, and I can't make it better, no matter how much I want to or how hard I try.

I am stuck with a huge dilemma. If I try to convince her she did a good job in raising her children, she will just resist and invalidate it. If, on the other hand, I agree with her that she was a bad mother, it would be untrue. What am I to do? Moving back away from her again, I realize that trying to convince her that she was a good mother isn't going to work. Rather, she needs to discover it for herself. Again, I need to get "me" out of the way and find a way to be of service to her.

"Grandma, can I ask you something?"

"What is it?" she quips, clutching her woolen blanket firmly with both hands.

"Grandma, do you know that only a *good* mother would think of what she had done for her kids? Only a good mother would think she hadn't done enough, while a bad mother wouldn't think about it at all."

She lay silent for a few moments and then turns to me and says softly, "I thought plenty about my kids. I worried about them day and night."

"So can you see, Granny, how much time you spent caring about them?"

After a long pause she bursts into tears. "It's true. I *was* a good mother. I never realized that. I cared so very much for my kids and for all you grandkids."

"Yes, Granny. You were wonderful with all of us and we are so thankful to have had you in our lives. Your children had their own paths and made their own choices. Let's leave any judgement up to God. You don't have to carry it any longer."

"Yes. I will leave it to God. It's not my place to judge," she replies quietly. "But I still don't understand why God hasn't come for me yet," she adds tenaciously.

"Grandma, I'm sorry God hasn't come for you yet. It must be painful for you, as I know how much you love God."

Her fists unclench and a wave of tears flood to her eyes. "Yes. Yes, I do love God. I love Him with all my heart."

As she speaks, I also realize how much I love God. A memory comes to mind of myself as a boy kneeling next to my bed. My grandmother is kneeling beside me, teaching me the Lord's prayer. "Our Father who art in heaven . . ." I speak it aloud to her and she begins to pray along with me, just like we did together so long ago. At the end of the prayer a calm comes over her and she relaxes into the bed. The tension releases from her arms and she exhales gently. She closes her eyes and gently squeezes my hand. This is a divine moment. I know I must leave soon, but I also know this is the last time I will ever see her. I reach over and kiss her on the cheek just as I did every time I said good-bye to her in the past. Tears well up again and my breathing constricts. Gasping for air and swallowing hard, I squeeze her hand one last time and stand up. Turning to walk away I cannot contain my sadness any longer.

"I love you so much, Grandma. I love you . . . so much," I blurt out, from the depths of my sorrow.

"I love you. Good-bye, my sweet grandson and God bless you."

Grace Oldham died that night. When I found out about her passing the next day, I reflected on our special time together. It was a great honor to have shared in her last few hours of life. By "staying out of the way," I feel that I received a wonderful gift. I discovered that to be of service to someone, I must be willing to set aside my own needs and feelings. I learned that when someone is upset or in pain, it's unwise to try and make it better for them. Although difficult, it's much better to allow them their pain and show them acceptance, love and support until they get through it themselves. My grandma will live in my heart forever and when it's time for me to meet *my* maker, my last breath will be filled with the remembrance of all the good things she stood for—courage, passion, humor, love, family and undying spiritual devotion.

As I wipe the moisture from my eyes, memories of my grandmother slowly fade away into the mists of the night. It is also the end of my revelations about the seven dimensions of knowing. How strange and serendipitous it is that the memories of losing my grandmother coincide with service, the final dimension of knowing. I look out over the valley and silently watch moonlit clouds creep up the mountainside. Visibility will soon be lost and I know I must move quickly to find shelter for the remainder of the night, but instead of acting on the thought, I remain transfixed by the advancing cloud cover. As I watch, I wonder if perhaps death is nothing more than a shroud of mist, an illusory cloud that advances upon us, temporarily blinding us to our immortal existence. And like the mountain that hides beneath the clouds, perhaps our soul also endures the chimera of death. In any case, I vow to stay grounded and in touch with the mountain of my soul when death consumes me. I shall stand firmly upon the pinnacle of spirit and stay connected with the earthstone of God.

Service, the last dimension of knowing, puts all the other dimensions into perspective by giving them meaning and purpose. What is the point of acquiring such grand knowledge if it doesn't further a cause or make a contribution? Even my most profound aspirations and insights have no value unless they have an influence or impact of some kind. I now understand that *Service* is the "vehicle" for the expression of all the other dimensions. When I am serving, *Humility* is real, *Eternality* is present, *Truth* is self-evident, *Passion* blazes, *Sovereignty* reigns and *Faith* is alive.

Stepping into the burn zone has delivered me seven remarkable understandings. I lean back into the Seat of the Condor, watching as the *Inca Fire* slowly fades into the darkness. There, in the waning embers, I see the same ancient faces that first greeted me when I discovered this sacred place. I bow to them in reverence as they slowly vanish into the night.

The Urubamba Valley filling with mist and clouds just before dark.

CHAPTER FIFTEEN

IN THE LIGHT OF THE SUN

Rays of Inca gold upon ancient stone
Warm this body, this heart and soul
May fire and earth and blessed skies
Deliver thine wisdom to infant eyes

As the massive cloud bank engulfs me, the stone below my feet provides solace and support. I cannot see past my nose so I have to crouch low and feel my way back down the huge flat boulder to seek shelter for the night. Sliding over the edge of the stone, I tumble down into the space between the three huge boulders. Luckily, I land squarely on my feet. In the blackness before me I use the tip of my right boot to locate the entrance to the enclave under the boulders. Finding it, I crouch down on my rump and slide through it and out into the narrow pathway that leads to the secret tunnel. The area is out of the wind so I search around for a flat spot to rest on. Visibility is less than a foot and I know that if I stray too far from where I am, I could fall over the edge and careen to my death. Lying back against the hard stone I pull my knees up to my chest and close my eyes.

I must have dozed off for a while, because when I awaken, my legs are frozen and my body is shaking uncontrollably. Stiff and racked with pain from lying on rock, I stretch out my legs and rub my hands briskly up and down their sides. Shoving my hands into my pockets I find the socks I'd forgotten to put back on after my afternoon climb. Although a welcome addition, they make little difference to my frozen feet. I've got at least three hours before dawn, so I'd better find a way to stay warm, or I'll freeze. The clumps of high grass to my left are my only option. Yanking bunches out by the roots, I pack them around my chilled body to prevent losing more body heat. Sitting up cross-legged, I stack the grass over my legs and tuck it firmly around my backside and underneath me. As I shiver under my makeshift cover, the self-flagellation starts.

"It's really cold. Why couldn't you at least have brought a sleeping bag? Or maybe some long underwear? Or even a blanket, for Christ's sake! Oh, no. You've got to be a spontaneous adventurer, don't you? You don't need the civilized accessories that normal people use. You're sittin' here freezing your ass off, and it serves you right. You have no right to complain about your situation when *you're* the one who was stupid enough to put yourself here. Maybe next time you'll think twice about being so rugged."

Thoroughly disgusted with myself, I cup my hands in front of my mouth to heat them with the lukewarm air from my lungs. The chill is working its way up my body from my frozen legs. My rump is completely numb and my stomach has an eerie coolness. It's now four o'clock in the morning, and I'm really miserable. I haven't had any sleep because of the incredible hardness of the ground and the constant chill in my body. Although I'm deeply grateful for the insights and wisdom I received from the *Light of the Masters*, all I can think about now is surviving until the sun comes up. It strikes me as kind of odd that, in one moment I can have inspiring visions that elevate me to new and profound understandings, and in the next I am a sniveling wimp filled with a litany of complaints and grievances.

Out of the corner of my left eye, I see a small flash of light. The dense cloud cover obscures its location so I stare into the general area to see if I can narrow it down.

"There it is again," I whisper to myself.

144

The light has a strange iridescent glow. A moment later, it flashes again, but now it appears closer. I watch intently, trying to spot its exact position. As the cloud thins slightly I'm able to both locate it and identify it. It's a tiny firefly resting on a spindly branch about three feet to my left. Its body is no more than a quarter-inch long and almost transparent. Its wings are tucked tightly against its back as it clutches firmly onto the spindly twig. Having plenty of time to study and observe, I begin to notice a consistent pattern to its illuminations. Whether coincidental or not, I discover that this little firefly lights up on every *thirteenth* beat of my heart. I know it's not true, but it sure seems like it's conveying to me, "Come on, Val Jon, look at me! I'm in the same dark cloud as you. I'm cold, uncomfortable and alone and yet I still light up. Why don't you light up with me? I'm not asking for inspiration with *every* heartbeat. All I ask is that you generate joy and light just one or two times out of thirteen."

Although this dialogue sounds a little odd, the Inca people believe that all creatures no matter how small or insignificant have the ability to communicate and inspire mankind through a deified language. I think I believe it too, because I'm becoming more inspired with each flash of light this little firefly generates. I suddenly have an astonishing realization. Here in front of me is another expression of the *Light of the Masters*. Although a lot less intense, the energy emanating from this tiny creature is the same energy generated by the *Inca Fire*. How can I stay miserable in the presence of such a display? Sitting up, I look forward to each flash. The more I appreciate its illuminations, the closer it gets. In a few minutes, the firefly is right next to me, displaying its lighthearted antics. I can't help but be embarrassed. Here I am, an "enlightened seeker" who has just received a lifetime worth of wisdom, and yet I'm generating less light and inspiration than this tiny little firefly— what a humbling lesson. I realize that even though the *Light of the Masters* exists "in the whole of things," I have to be the one who generates it and brings it out.

This frozen night on the mountaintop is my first test of applying the Seven Dimensions of Knowing. Sitting here in the cold darkness, I realize it will be easy enough to stay aware of the seven dimensions when I'm inspired to do so, but what about when things are the pits, like now? What about when I feel rotten, miserable and depressed? Will I remember to "flash" then? The answer had better be "yes" or the whole experience I just had is worth little. There have been many times in my life when I've had great insights and understandings, but because I didn't apply them, they became useless. It's knowing all the right things to do, but when it comes right down to it, not doing the right things. It's knowing I should have more patience with my colleagues and then wanting to throttle them when they don't handle things quickly enough.

As I watch this little firefly, I imagine standing next to a huge bonfire. The flames shoot up high into the night, and my hands are extended to gather warmth. As the flames die down, I move closer to stay warm. Then as they wane even further, I find myself almost on top of them to keep warm. "Who's in charge of stoking this fire?" I ask. There's no reply. "How am I going to stay warm if somebody doesn't bring some wood?" Again, there's no reply. Then it dawns on me. Nobody's going to stoke the fire for me. If I want to stay warm, I'd better get out there and chop some wood and stoke the fire myself. This little digression shows me that "chopping wood and stoking the fire" is synonymous with actively practicing the Seven Dimensions of Knowing in my daily life.

That's what this little inspirational firefly is doing, it's generating its own light and heat. It isn't waiting for someone else to do it, it's taking the initiative and using its natural talents. Even though such creatures are genetically disposed to flash in the dark, it's still a great lesson. Just because I'm not hard-wired to flash in the darkness of my own life doesn't mean I can't do it. If this tiny creature has the power to create its own light, then I certainly can. I will take a lesson from this tiny winged creature, and remember to "flash" regardless of the circumstances in my life—especially when I'm caught in dark clouds.

Now that the issue of self-generating my inspiration is resolved, my discomfort is no longer an issue. The sun will rise in due time and my body will recover soon enough. Until then, it's my challenge to create my own light. As dawn approaches, I pull my legs out from under my massive grass cocoon and slowly stand up. As I brush the grass and debris from my clothes, a smile comes to my chapped face. Images of the Inca Fire, the Seat of the Condor and the tiny firefly reverberate in my mind. I am blessed to have received their wisdom. The profound insight and understanding I now possess is well worth the stiffness and chill of the night. Shaking my head in amazement, I climb back up to the summit to greet the morning sun. I scale the large flat-topped boulder again and stretch out on its massive surface to receive the warmth of the sun's blazing Inca gold.

Rays of sunlight stream through crisp, cool air, illuminating the gray stones and green terraces of Machu Picchu. The Peruvian mountainsides shed their ghostly shadows to let their white granite faces gleam in the morning light. My body quakes and shivers as its frigid legacy begins to thaw. I've just spent fourteen hours—a mere half-day—on the summit of Wayna Picchu. Yet I feel as though I've gained a lifetime of wisdom. Lying back on the cold stone, I let the sun bathe me in its warmth and light. No wonder so many civilizations through the ages have worshipped the sun. It's a miracle of creation that brings life to every living thing its rays touch. It's also a magnificent example of constant self-generation. Blazing with eternal passion, it endures boldly in the vast expanse of space, shining brightly for eons, never once relying on another celestial body for assurance or support.

In my moments of reflection, a gentle wind swirls around me, reminding me that I will soon have to leave this high place. Part of me wants to stay forever and part of me is anxious to get on with my life. After warming up I stand and turn in every direction, drinking in the grace and majesty all around me. My eyes are lenses for the film of my soul, and with them I capture the images before me. I take the camera out of my jacket pocket and carefully position it on the high rocky ledge. I set the automatic timer, and then race back to pose at the Seat of the Condor. Now I have a physical picture of this place as well. Sitting in the sacred perch one last time, I thank all those who came before me and welcome all those who will follow. An image of the familiar red and yellow flames appears in my mind. There, between the ribbons of light in the middle of the burn zone, I see the faces of the ancients who shared the *Master's Light* with me. Perhaps my face will someday join them. If so, it will be a humble face, a kind face, a face that shines with the light of the *Inca Fire!*

CHAPTER SIXTEEN

REFLECTIONS OF THE LIGHT

Ancient sun, bright mirror
I, too, like all my ancestors,
embrace your warmth
and then, am no more

I've made my way down the mountain and back to the Machu Picchu ruins by nine o'clock. Hesitating for just a moment next to the guard shack, I'm relieved to find that the security staff is not yet on post. Crawling back over the large rock shoulder of Mini Picchu, I cross the Central Plaza and head for the Hitching Post of the Sun. As I wait for Alberto and Eliceu to arrive, I visually trace my ascent route up the face of Wayna Picchu to the top. It's an amazing sight. The rich green foliage contrasts with the white and gray granite in a vivid display. Far atop the highest ridge I can make out the outline of the massive flat boulder that holds the Seat of the Condor. Gazing up at the very spot I had earlier been looking down from gives me an eerie feeling. How strange, to be in two different locations in such a short time. For a moment, it feels as though I'm standing in both places at once.

In the next moment, I recall a vision I had the previous day on this very spot. The image was that of seeing two priests engaged in some kind of "remote connection." One of them stood on the summit of Wayna Picchu, while the other was right here where

149

I'm now standing. Could my vision have been a premonition of this moment? After the night I just had, anything is possible.

Alberto, Eliceu and Cleide, a friend of Eliceu's, arrive just after nine-thirty. Cleide had also participated in the ceremonies the night before and is eager to talk about her experiences. A native Brazilian in her early thirties, she speaks only a little English. Like Alberto and Eliceu, Cleide has a genuine warmth about her. The people of South America are unpretentious and can establish rapport almost immediately with strangers. After our initial greetings, we sit down together and begin sharing our experiences. They start by recounting their experiences from the previous night. Over a hundred people from around the world had joined in the festivities under the full moon. There were four or five different events going on in the ruins at the same time. Activities included prayer, group discussion, meditation, dance and poetry reading. As my friends talk about the ceremonies, I recall having seen clusters of lights moving through different sections of the ruins from my high perch. Eliceu's group had performed meditation ceremonies with a small group in the southern section, while the Church of Universal Peace conducted their events near the Three Windows on the western slope. At least two other groups gathered in the Industrial and Residential Sectors for their ceremonies.

Now it's my turn to share. I start by recounting my stealthy maneuvers around the security guards, my vision of the Inca priest entering my body, and witnessing the destruction of Machu Picchu by lightning bolts. Next, I share a few of the hair-raising moments during my ascent to the summit. Since they hadn't been to the top of Wayna Picchu, they appreciate hearing about the lofty ancient ruins and the hidden, cavelike tunnel that leads to the Seat of the Condor. I also relay to them my visions of the *Inca Fire* and the Seven Dimensions of Knowing. Rather than recounting all of my memories, however, I opt for reading the seven inspired passages that came to me. Finally, I tell them about freezing my butt off in the early morning hours and my encounter with the inspiring little firefly.

The Seven Dimensions of Knowing interested them most. We spent more than an hour discussing the inspired messages and later went into greater detail at a restaurant back in Aguas Calientes. There was something remarkable about our conversation: because the inspired messages were somewhat philosophical, the four of us perceived them differently. The more we discussed our insights about each of the dimensions, the clearer their utility became. The material was so rich and inspiring, our conversation took on a life of its own and led each of us to our own inherent wisdom. As we grappled with the passages, we seemed to tap into a soulful part of ourselves that not only could decipher the material, but also "knew" about it in ways that surprised us. I've summarized many of our insights in the following paragraphs and have added a few points for clarification to bring the passages to life. Please don't feel that you have to use only my interpretations, as there are as many meanings as there are minds to conceive them. Once you've read the material, however, you may want to think about sharing the seven dimensions with others, as discussing the information seems to help integrate it.

HUMILITY:

Humility itself has no form, its presence is invisible to the naked eye. It is visible only to the naked soul and the humble heart, which ever longs for the light yet still beats with undying devotion within the body, never seeing the light of day. Inside this earthstone, too, is darkness filled with the Light of the Masters. May solids hold together ever densely for us to stand upon as they emanate the light through their crystal gemlike forms.

The first part of this passage, *Humility itself has no form,* suggests that humility doesn't have to look a certain way. Many people have set images of what it means to be humble. Such images include kneeling in reverence, selfless prayer, meekness and even subservience. Although these things might represent humility, it may be more useful for each of us to seek its true meaning within the crucible of our own soul and, once found, aspire to it.

The next section, *only to the naked soul and the humble heart, which ever longs for the light yet still beats with undying devotion within the body, never seeing the light of day,* spoke to us of vulnerability. The term *naked soul* has a double meaning. From one perspective, naked is to be unclothed or without covering, thus representing openness and vulnerability. This makes sense because humility begins with a willingness to drop our defensive walls and reveal the tenderness within our hearts. From another perspective, *naked soul* could mean that the nature of the soul itself is unclothed. In other words, it is bare, unencumbered by mortal protocol, void of character or garb. Rather than being a *thing*, it could be a vastness or infinite space which, by its very nature, is connected to what we consider divine.

Some may say that being vulnerable can be risky or even dangerous. This would be true if one believed the soul could be damaged or killed. But for those who know the soul is indeed vast and eternal, this fear doesn't exist.

Undying devotion near the end of the passage further illuminates that humility requires an ongoing expression of openness and selfless faith. This insight fits well for me. My experience of calling my father after my mountain climb was one of the toughest "ongoing expressions of openness" I had ever engaged in. It was also one of the most blessed because I freed myself from negative feelings about him and reestablished a healthy relationship that has blossomed over the years since our reconnection.

Inside this earthstone too is darkness filled with the Light of the Masters. May solids hold together ever densely for us to stand upon as they emanate the light through their crystal gemlike forms. This part of the passage is more enigmatic, but the themes of *earthstone* and *earth* suggest that humility may be like a *humus* or fertile soil for spiritual development. To be sure, without the soil of humility, few will ever gain access to the divine.

ETERNALITY:

The notion of mastery, in light of the truth, can only be known through the resilience of the soul and open embrace of open embrace.

Although a strange word, to me eternality represents infinite vastness or *eternalness*. Keeping the eternal in mind, let's look at the first phrase, *resilience of the soul*. From this context, *resilience* seems to refer not just to mere endurance, but to infinite strength or indestructibility. If the soul is indeed infinite and indestructible, then the more we stay connected with it, the more resilient we become. My experience of being healed with Sai Baba's holy ash convinced me that infinite power is available to us if we are willing to seek it out.

Next let's examine *open embrace of open embrace*. It's clear that *open embrace* is a willingness to accept what life gives us, but *of open embrace* is confusing. When we look more deeply, however, we see that opening only once is insufficient. There have been many times when I was initially open to something and then closed up like a clam. *Open embrace of open embrace*, means reopening, again and again and again—especially when we don't want to or feel justified in staying closed. During our discussion we noticed moments when we closed to each other's ideas. It was odd to talk about staying open while feeling closed. Each time we noticed a closure, we commented on it and consciously opened to each other again.

TRUTH:

Seek not what you will never find—for your destiny shall be never to know in the way you desire. Rather, look directly into the Inca Fire and remember the truth of what has always been known.

This passage has great significance. To *never know in the way you desire* is provocative but irrefutable. I can't count the times when I've wanted to know why something happened the way it did, only to be left scratching my head in confusion or disbelief. Wanting answers isn't such a bad trait when it comes to the practicalities of life, but there are times when answers just won't provide us with what we really need. Sometimes confusion, self-doubt and moments of density are of greater service to us. (Depending, of course, on just how long one remains in these states.)

We are a society of solution-oriented problem solvers. Give us a problem and we'll solve it. If we can't solve it, we'll find someone who can, and if they can't fix it, we'll create a temporary solution until a more credible one comes along. We want to know things the *way* we want to know them and *when* we want to know them. Force us to know something before we are good and ready, and we get frustrated, confused or humiliated. Keep us in the dark too long, and we become impatient, childish and nasty. The passage *never know in the way you desire,* clearly points out that life will give us our answers when life is ready. And if we try to force the issue, life will teach us about being too pushy and controlling.

The other part of the passage, *remember the truth of what has always been known,* clarifies truth even further. Remembering truth is quite different from learning it. We possess a knowledge of truth within us and, given the right conditions, we can access that truth and apply it in our lives. This Socratic principle makes a lot of sense to me, especially keeping in mind Reverend Mumon's words, "In the west, you place more importance on telling the truth than knowing it." When I'm telling the truth, I'm repeating what other people have taught me. When I *know* the truth, I am accessing my own innate ability to discern what is true.

PASSION:

The sun and the moon and the stars make tonight not the master's light, but the illusory light of hope, inspiration and illumination for mortal eyes to finally ask, And from whence does this radiant golden beauty arise? And so, behind the moon, within the sun, and throughout the stellars bright, the Light of the Masters evokes its Passion from the essential nature of all things—sparked by the paradoxical desire to expand, yet the need to belong, by the orbits of freedom and the gravity of grace, by the force of mystery and the comfort of certainty, by the curse of doubt and the bliss of faith. The Light of the Masters is evoked by the union of compassion and fear, the tension between creation and destruction, and the dance between life and death. It is born of the force which draws the stars apart and holds them together, by the poles of eternity, matter and space.

This esoteric mouthful requires a bit more discussion. Let's examine it a section at a time. *The sun and the moon and the stars make tonight not the master's light, but the illusory light of hope.* The *illusory light* in this phrase refers to desire, the shallow aspect of passion, which includes lust, greed, hunger and need. Many people confuse passion with desire when, in fact, they are as different as night and day. The next sentence helps clarify the difference.

Behind the moon, within the sun and throughout the stellars bright, the Light of the Masters evokes its passion from the essential nature of all things. Passion, unlike desire is a universal phenomenon that functions on a grand, even cosmic scale. From a cosmic perspective, passion could express itself in everything from sparking the chemical reaction within a tiny firefly to infusing gravity with the power to command celestial bodies. No wonder I was accused of being mediocre during my visit to the Joshua Tree desert. Embracing this kind of passion puts a whole new spin on life.

The next section illuminates some key attributes of passion. *Sparked by the paradoxical desire to expand yet the need to belong, by the orbits of freedom and the gravity of grace, by the force of mystery and the comfort of certainty, by the curse of doubt and the bliss of faith.*

Passion is paradoxical and can create dilemmas and problems. Getting swept up in the raptures of unbridled passion is titillating and even gratifying; however, in a single moment it can also destroy what took years to create. Passion is like a spark of energy that jumps between reason and emotion, short-circuiting objectivity.

To clarify passion's universal and paradoxical nature, look at the next section. *It is born of the force which draws the stars apart and holds them together, by the poles of eternity, matter and space.*

Like the cosmic force of gravity, passion has immense paradoxical power. When revealed in its wholeness, it can inspire us, fulfill us, and even endow us with universal understanding. When misinterpreted as mere desire and lust, however, it has the power to tear worlds apart like the poles of eternity. Each of us must choose our own perception of passion and let the stars fall as they will.

SOVEREIGNTY:

Be alone again in your Sovereignty—that we may be together, you and I. Be simple again, that we may talk of essential things. Make not wants and desires, for in their absence you will truly seek and surely find what has been known by us from the alpha to the omega, what has inspired the mind of God to create and then destroy.

This passage is filled with insight and inspiration. It is the one my group spent the most time on because of the eye-opening realizations. We all agreed that with respect to *being alone,* most people avoid it. In a demanding world, we reach for the distractions of television, movies, sex, food, drugs and alcohol. Although these follies provide temporary gratification, they also get old and, at some point, fail to provide the fulfillment we seek. Mid-life crisis is, in part, the realization that everything that "did it for us before," no longer does. Those who realize there must be more to life than the next hit of pleasure, may indulge at times, but in addition they seek a deeper kind of fulfillment. Sovereignty means having dominion over—command over—being autonomous, self-reliant and generative. Sovereignty differs from independence in that it not only embodies individuality, it also possesses the ability to self-start, create and sustain.

Be alone again in your Sovereignty—that we may be together, you and I. Be simple again that we may talk of essential things. The words, *Be alone again* ask us to shed our external distractions and return to that sovereign and simple part of ourselves, to the inner sanctuary that no one else can access. There are many paths to the sanctuary of self, including meditation, prayer, dance, art and communion with nature. Whatever the path, the important thing is to make the time needed to return to ourselves now and then.

The phrase, *that we may be together, you and I,* has at least two meanings. Like the reunion referred to above, we must reconnect with our own unique identity; however, not one's persona, or image of self, but one's "true self." This true self has remained unchanged, an ageless and shapeless traveling companion that accompanies us from childhood to adulthood. It's the self that exists outside of time and belief and even feeling. It's the self that observes and listens to its own thoughts, its senses and perceptions. You know, it's the self that's says, "I know what he means," "I'm not quite getting it," or "This is bunk." Regardless of your internal chatter, the *you* that just had *that* thought is the "self" to which this passage refers.

Also, the phrase has more to do with a *divine* connection than it does with a *self*-connection. Some might contend they are one and the same, but for purposes of clarifying this passage, I'd like to keep them distinct. "You and I" as a divine connection takes on a "thou and I," context. "Thou" becomes the personification of whatever the "I" believes is divine. I could, for example, believe that God is divine, or the Universe, or Spirit, or Energy or Superior Intelligence. The point is, whatever I consider divine becomes "thou" in the phrase. This relationship with "thou" ensures that we will never be alone. In both perspectives, a relationship with self and a connection with the divine is necessary to become sovereign.

Make not wants and desires, for in their absence you will truly seek and surely find what has been known by us from the alpha to the omega, what has inspired the mind of God to create and then destroy. In this phrase, two insights can be seen. *Make not wants and desires . . .*

157

Make not is very different from *have not.* The passage doesn't suggest we should not "have" wants and desires, but that rather, we shouldn't "make" any more than we already have. Clearly this phrase illuminates avoiding the trappings of excess and addiction.

The second insight is a bit harder to grasp. *What has been known by us from the alpha to the omega, what has inspired the mind of God to create and then destroy.* This mysterious and somewhat ominous statement is baffling. The snippet, *what has been known by us,* suggests that there are keepers of knowledge—so who are they? There is no answer at this time. *From the alpha to the omega,* is a familiar phrase about eternity, meaning from the beginning to the end. Finally, *what has inspired the mind of God to create and then destroy,* although moving, is a bit frightening.

If we keep in perspective that we are examining the dimension of sovereignty, and that part of its nature is to establish and nurture a divine connection, *the mind of God* is a viable terminal. But what has sovereignty to do with possessing the power *to create and then destroy?* This is the crux of the matter. To be sovereign, we must constantly self-generate and create. We must have the courage to initiate, embrace and release at will. The Hawaiian Kahuna, Sam Lono illuminated this point well for me with his words, "come, stay, go." Creating, (initiating) and destroying, (releasing) are essential components of the cycle of life. Although sovereignty does not give us dominion *over* the cycle of life, it most certainly can give us command *within* it.

FAITH:

> *Look not for what you will never see, for your eyes deceive your senses and your senses fool your mind. Instead, climb to a high place away from time. Make simple your mind and open your heart to Faith. Then touch the earthstone of eternity and the Light of the Masters will come to you and illuminate the way.*

The first sentence, *Look not for what you will never see, for your eyes deceive your senses and your senses fool your mind,* shows us that our senses, although wonderful and vital to shaping our experience, fall short in their ability to detect the divine. Experience, the very thing we use as our basis for validating reality, is limited by its reliance on tangible evidence. The divine, however, is not tangible and, since faith is a divine principle, it exists outside the purview of experience. Scientists constantly confront this problem when trying to explain the expansiveness of the universe or the inconsistencies between cosmology and quantum physics. The more they try to conceptualize the divine, the less they seem to perceive it.

Instead, climb to a high place away from time. Make simple your mind and open your heart to Faith. This section reinforces many of the ideas already discussed. *Climb to a high place* might mean physical height, but *away from time* suggests we direct our attention toward spiritual wisdom. It also correlates with the "self-connection/ divine connection" of sovereignty. *Make simple your mind* is clearing the mind of thoughts, similar to meditation techniques that minimize mental distractions. *Open your heart to faith* directs us to set aside our mental chatter and open our emotional selves so that faith can gain entrance to our hearts. When we put the sections together, we find three steps for accessing faith: aspiring to the divine; clearing a pathway to it; and opening the heart to receive it.

The last section of the passage beautifully summarizes the process for accessing faith. *Then touch the earthstone of eternity and the Light of the Masters will come to you and illuminate the way.* The *earthstone* can be interpreted as the base, foundation, or grounding point of eternity. *Eternity* represents unbounded spirit and faith, and because it's so vast, we need a solid point of connection to it. Just where this connection point or earthstone can be found is a matter of speculation. I find it high atop mountains and by leaping from bridge railings. For others, it could be in the faces of their children, in their place of worship, in a park, in deep meditation, or even while reading a great novel. Wherever the earthstone may be, making a connection with it is what will *illuminate the way.*

When the way is illuminated for us, we don't need to worry about finding it. This was a big relief for me when it came to the

Seven Dimensions of Knowing. Although they are wonderful principles, filled with inspiration, trying to remember all of them at the same time seemed a daunting task. When faith is present, its companion dimensions are with us whether we're aware of them or not. That's not to say we should assume a passive role. We still must consciously engage with each of the dimensions in order to stay present to the *Master's Light*. My little firefly made that point vividly clear to me.

SERVICE:

> *The Service of the Master's Light exists beyond the mind and senses and outside of time—in a flash of revelation we suddenly see what we have been blind to all our lives. Has not light been shed on what we were to see all along? What illumination then serves us and enables us to see? The Light of the Masters is not outside to behold, nor is it inside to touch. It is on no 'side' but rather—in the whole of things.*

Service gives all the other dimensions of knowing purpose and meaning. Without action and contribution, principles such as humility, truth and faith are nothing more than superficial commodities of "cosmetic consciousness."

The Service of the Master's Light exists beyond the mind and senses and outside of time. This clarifies the nature of service. Because of its metaphysical orientation, the act of serving occurs within a divine context rather than a personal one. This insight discourages the selfish desire to take credit for acts of service. When we serve, we do so without arrogance, obligation or expectation. That's not to say we shouldn't assist people from time to time. Assistance is about helping, solving problems, making things easier for others. It is an important part of humanitarianism. But assistance and service are not the same. When we serve, rather than trying to fix things *for* people, we open a channel in concert *with* them that empowers them to make a connection with whatever they consider to be divine—and through that connection, they gain their own sense of faith and power. I am reminded of my last moments with my grandmother before she died. Every time I tried to help her, she resisted. The moment I opened myself to being of service, she discovered her own truths and found peace.

The next section of the passage reveals the power of service and how it actually manifests. *In a flash of revelation we suddenly see what we have been blind to all our lives. Has not light been shed on what we were to see all along?* True service manifests as a *flash of revelation* that blinds us with its intensity in one moment, and gives us new eyes to see in the next. Service can be anything from tender and loving to brutally empowering. Although I have been served through tenderness, I have also been served when others have been honest with me about my pettiness, ego or blindness. Although my self-image may have been bruised in the process, I invariably became a better person for it.

It's not only people who can serve us in this way; life itself can. For those who are unwilling to allow others to serve them, life steps in and does the job. I'm reminded of a quote by the German philosopher Karlfried Graf Dürckheim that illustrates this point:

> It is in the extremes like imminent death, ultimate absurdity, and total isolation that we are given the strength to do something that the natural ego cannot do: accept the unacceptable. We may accept it only for a split second, but this is enough—enough for a crack to open briefly in the carapace of our limitations letting the limitless stream in.

The next two questions in the passage clarify the "timelessness" of service. *Has not light been shed on what we were to see all along? What illumination then serves us and enables us to suddenly see?* The lessons of service we receive have always been available, but we get them only when we are ready or willing. There is both comfort and embarrassment in this truth. It is comforting to know that all our lessons will hang around even if we ignore them. The embarrassment is, "Why does it take so long for me to get it at times?"

The last section of the passage holds the most important aspect of service. *The Light of the Masters is not outside to behold, nor is it inside to touch. It is on no 'side' but rather—in the whole of things.* The key to understanding this concept lies in the phrase, *no 'side.'* When we are truly being of service, there is no "server" or "servee." All roles vanish and in their place arises *the whole of things*, a divine relationship that transcends separation. As service occurs, both parties receive contributions, regardless of their perspective roles. I'm again reminded of the experience with my grandmother. Who served whom in that exchange? She was served by realizing that she *was* a good mother and by surrendering to her relationship with God. I was served by setting my own selfish needs aside, opening my heart and getting in touch with my own mortality.

Service exists *in the whole of things.* When we are served and when we serve others, a wholeness is present—a rich and fulfilling sense of connection, unity and divinity. To be of service to others is one of the most profound of human expressions. Service, too, gives life to the other dimensions of knowing. It inspires *Humility*, illuminates *Eternality*, evokes *Truth*, fosters *Sovereignty* and celebrates *Faith*. The more we serve, the more the *Light of the Masters* streams into our lives and into the lives of those we touch.

CHAPTER SEVENTEEN

ILLUMINATIONS FOR THE SOUL

To the West this wise old Condor soars
Carrying these souls to heavenly stars . . .
Of our ancestor's home, that eternal place
Where spirits and souls dwell in grace
Where spirits and souls form the faceless face

Deciphering the Seven Dimensions of Knowing has proved a rewarding and insightful process. As I studied the passages in more detail and began integrating them into my daily life, I realized two important things: First, the more I engaged with them, the greater the positive influence they had on my behaviors and my general outlook; second, there was something mystical and universal about the dimensions in that my realizations were more like remembrances than they were new understandings. Experiencing the Seven Dimensions of Knowing from this perspective has not only made it easy to apply them in my daily life, it has created a momentum to discover more about them.

Although I had learned a lot from studying the seven dimensions, I sensed they contained many more secrets. For weeks I struggled to unlock the meanings hidden within the inspired passages. Then one evening while lying in front of my fireplace, I had a revelation. As I studied my original notes from the expedition, my eyes happened to catch a translucent shadow dancing on the hearth in front of me. As I followed the flickering shadowy lines, I noticed they converged at one of the andirons that hold the burning oak logs. There was something strange about the shadow that commanded my attention. Rather than just one image, I noticed it was composed of three images "fanned out" in close proximity. Each of the three images had the same shape, but possessed a slightly different shade or density. I had seen such shadows before and knew they were created by multiple light sources shining on a single object. In this case, the flames provided a fiery array of light sources responsible for the triple shadow.

Watching the interplay between the three images, it hit me. Hidden within the abstract burn zone of the *Light of the Masters* was an ancient road map. Not a map that outlines physical terrain, but one that illuminates specific behaviors for deepening and maturing the soul. By "soul," I refer to that paradoxical part of us that possesses both human and divine characteristics. The soul, from this perspective, is the nexus where mortality and spirit intersect, where logic and mystery merge and where what we hold as sacred imbues our consciousness with reverence, inspiration and humility.

The threefold shadow from my fireplace illuminated an important connection between the Seven Dimensions of Knowing and the soul. I realized that each of the dimensions contained three specific behaviors—behaviors that, when emulated properly, deepen both our humanity and our spirituality. Dimension by dimension I identified the behaviors, until I had accounted for all twenty-one. What a discovery. These twenty-one behaviors suddenly transformed the seven good-natured but abstract dimensions into a valuable road map for personal and spiritual development. There are hundreds of behaviors that could be identified for such development. I have chosen only those I believe correlate with the Seven Dimensions of Knowing. I offer these behaviors to you as suggestions rather than doctrines.

It may be valuable to look at each dimension yourself and identify the behaviors you feel are most important in your life. That way, you can create your own map for development rather than rely on my suggestions. Whatever way, if you engage in the following behaviors you're sure to see positive results. My list includes each of the Seven Dimensions of Knowing, their three specific behaviors and some definitions and clarifications for purposes of application.

Humility: Openness, Vulnerability & Compassion

Openness permits access, entrance or exit. When we are open, we possess unconstrained freedom. Emotional openness expresses itself as a willingness to experience, listen, feel, engage and interact. Openness applies to oneself as well as to being with others. Being open with oneself is being in touch with inner feelings, senses and capabilities. When we are open to ourselves, we are honest and forthright. Denial, rationalization and justification play only a minor role in our behavior, and we pay little or no attention to our self image or how others perceive us. Part of being open is assessing the degree of openness we possess in any moment. It is possible to be open to being closed. In fact, it is this state that often initiates new openings. Without being aware that we are closed in any given moment, we have little motivation to open up again. Next time you find yourself closed, try opening to the question, "is being closed what I really want in this moment?"

Vulnerability is being open and sensitive to attack or criticism, during which hurt, pain and emotional damage can occur. Vulnerability is being susceptible to what others may say or do. Vulnerability is the quality of sharing the "inside" of yourself with what is "outside" yourself. It is the connection between that which is hidden and that which is exposed. There is an inherent connection between all things, and vulnerability is the state in which that connection is visible and tangible. When I am vulnerable, I expose the invisible relationship between myself and another or others. The ability to say "Ouch, that hurts," is an expression of vulnerability and a recognition of the fact that we *are* connected at some level. If I withhold my feelings, I am saying that we are not connected and that you have no influence over me. If being vulnerable opens us to attack or criticism, then why would we want to develop this behavior? Let's keep in mind that we are trying to deepen humility. Without some degree of vulnerability, humility is impossible. When we are hurt, emotionally or physically, we reexamine what is important to us and open ourselves to being humbled, either by choice or necessity.

Compassion is empathy and understanding for the plight of others. Although many would think that sympathy fits into this definition, it actually doesn't. Sympathy says, "I feel sorry for you that you are so sad." Empathy says, "I feel sadness with you." It is this "with you" experience that defines the true nature of compassion. Compassion says, "Sadness fills us, let us embrace it together." When we have compassion for others, we are acknowledging our relatedness and connection with them. We understand that we either have already experienced something similar, or may in the future have to confront the very thing they are now dealing with. To deepen our sense of compassion, we must have a direct connection with a deeper part of ourselves, a divine part that knows we are intrinsically connected to others and that embracing our pains, joys and sorrows is a collaborative challenge.

Eternality: Resilience, Endurance & Indestructibility

Resilience is the ability to bounce back after taking a hit. It is the tenacity and strength to recover time and time again from circumstances that befall us. Resilience means being fresh, new and vivid in every moment. It is the ability to channel our energies and restock our resources so they are available to us whenever we need them. Emotional resilience expresses itself in the ability to stay engaged, deal with problems, confront issues and follow through with honesty and completeness. A component of initiation is also associated with resilience. Being resilient means stepping forward of our own accord, making ourselves visible and our ideas known.

Endurance is long-standing fortitude. It is resilience stretched over time. To endure means to hold up for the long haul, to maintain the energy required to confront infinite distress, fatigue and hardship. Emotional endurance is the ability to not only tolerate but actively embrace what we abhor and derive energy from it, rather than be drained by it. There is an element of constant rebirth in endurance. We may figuratively die in one moment so we can be reborn in the next. Although antithetical, death sometimes is the pathway to endurance—not physical death per se, but the death perhaps of ego or attachments that keep us small and ineffective. It was the philosopher Nietzsche who said, "We must die many times in order to live."

Indestructibility is the knowledge that, although our body will perish, our spirit can never be destroyed. Being indestructible is possessing the awareness that who we are is much greater than our identity. When "I" expands beyond the confines of "me," and includes "you," and even "thou," the awareness of eternality becomes available. Indestructibility gives us the courage to face life, take risks and constantly redefine who we are and what we are capable of. It doesn't have to give license to heedlessness, rather, it can empower us to more freely participate in the mystery and wonder of being alive. It is often through the loss of what we thought was permanent that we come to know the eternal. The death of a loved one, the loss of a relationship, or a major life change can bring us the awareness that everything we thought was permanent is actually transitory and that it is only our soul and spirit that endures through time.

Truth: Authenticity, Groundedness & Objectivity

Authenticity is the act of being genuine, real and honest. When we are authentic, we are trustworthy and straightforward in our deeds and actions. Authenticity requires the willingness to speak the truth and live by the truths we speak. Being authentic doesn't equate with perfection. In fact, when we come clean about our dishonesty, we demonstrate authenticity. Increasing our level of authenticity requires a willingness to honestly express what we feel or think in a responsible manner.

Groundedness is having a solid foundation. It is developed through establishing a firm base and employing a consistent approach. Being grounded yields a sense of equanimity, peace and stability. When we are grounded, we can stretch out farther into the mysteries of life and reinvent aspects of personal creativity and freedom. The more solid a foundation we create, the more our constructs and intentions will endure the test of time. Developing groundedness doesn't require mere modesty or conservatism. Quite the contrary. Groundedness actually requires a rigorous examination of our conservative beliefs and assumptions. In fact, until we have the courage to challenge the pillars of our faith, the legacy of our forefathers and the depth of our resolve, we remain on uncertain ground. It is the conscious act of doing violence to our mediocrity and predictability that crumbles our illusions of certainty, thus delivering us to the bedrock of our own soul.

Objectivity is being without bias or prejudice. It is the ability to distinguish between what one perceives as real and what is real. When we are objective, we function outside the influence of our own needs, agendas or desires. Objectivity gives us the ability to inquire, examine and explore with a commitment to empirical data rather than subjective interpretation. Knowing facts has great power, especially when they have been tested against credible sources. Objectivity should not take the place of conjecture, as both have a place within us; however, that place should be side by side, not one before the other.

Passion: Enthusiasm, Inspiration & Aspiration

Enthusiasm is to be possessed or inspired by a supernatural or divine force. This inner spiritedness expresses itself as intense interest and inspired action. Enthusiasm is created from within. Generating enthusiasm is a function of contemplating what we consider valuable, allowing ourselves to be moved or touched emotionally, and then expressing our experience openly with others. Enthusiasm has no specific form. It might look like jumping up and down wildly, or it could be a silent expression of prayer or grace, or it could even manifest as subtle tears of joy or appreciation.

Inspiration is the act of "breathing in" something which causes us to be moved in a positive or creative manner. Unlike enthusiasm, inspiration comes to us from external sources. It is when life itself or someone in life demonstrates a superlative quality, deed or action that we become inspired. Inspiration, in addition to being a powerful emotional experience, also can spark behavioral changes that move us to model the qualities which initially inspired us.

Inspiration can also exist beyond the scope of emotion or feeling. For example, one's faith or spiritual resolve can be deepened through existential forms of inspiration. The inspiration may not register as emotional insight, but through engaging in more meaningful prayer or meditation, or through a subtle yet powerful shift in one's appreciation of nature.

Aspiration is the act of "exhaling" or expressing a strong desire or ambition. It is our espoused dreams, desires and ultimate wants. Aspirations are different from goals. A goal is something we have outlined to accomplish through cognitive planning and execution, while an aspiration is a magical ideal we yearn for, a captivating notion that enchants our souls and liberates our minds. When we aspire to something, we imagine ourselves standing in the midst of its power, and in the wonder of crafting and shaping it into reality.

Having aspirations requires being honest about what we want and being moved to achieve it. Many people suppress their aspirations because they have abandoned or denied what is important to them. Apathy is the enemy of aspiration because it inhibits our positive energy and stifles our ability to self-motivate. History can also inhibit our ability to aspire. Past failures often steal the thunder of our passion because we see them as evidence that we cannot or should not aspire to anything. "We will never realize it anyway so why even try?" To infuse new life into our aspirations, we must reassess what we want through acknowledging and releasing any apathy or denial.

Sovereignty: Respect, Autonomy & Power

Respect comes from the Latin roots "re," meaning "again," and "respicere," meaning "to look back on." From this perspective, respect means "to re-look." To re-look at what? The conclusions, decisions or assumptions we may be holding about ourselves or others. In the normal course of events we are taught that respect is something earned. I'll respect you if you deserve it. You've got to prove to me that you are worthy of my respect and, if you do, then maybe I'll give it to you. But the definition of "re-looking" expands this construct. Rather than respect just being something earned, it also can be something given. When I am willing to re-look and release my judgments or conclusions, I am giving respect. The value in being able to freely give respect lies in establishing trust and facilitating a developmental process either for oneself or for others. If I am constantly judging you or making you jump through "respect hoops," I risk alienating you and cutting off any chance for positive movement in our relationship. It's the times when I was given respect, especially when I didn't deserve it, that I was moved or influenced the most.

Autonomy is the state of existing or functioning independently from another or others. When we are autonomous, we have the ability to make our own way and are not dependent on others for assistance, guidance or support. Autonomy doesn't mean we should separate or isolate ourselves from others, but that we are capable of functioning without them if we need to. An important fact is to know that just because people have successfully made their own way in life doesn't automatically make them autonomous. Autonomy requires much more than physical independence. Until we become "true to ourselves" emotionally, mentally and spiritually, we remain trapped at some level within the confines of dependence. Many people have moved thousands of miles away from their families to escape the dynamics of control and domination, only to find that they have carried the curse of their childhood across the country with them.

Power, from the Latin root "potere," means "to be able." Being powerful means having the ability to initiate, engage and follow through. Power and force are not the same. To practice being powerful, we must be willing to set aside our need to control, dominate and manipulate. Unlike control, power relies on one's resolve to make things happen through intention, dedication and collaboration. Although power is a personal phenomenon, it can never be "owned" by anyone. The moment it is coveted for purposes of credit or ego gratification, it transforms into control. Power also need not be flamboyant, dramatic or extreme. Think of it as the deep currents of an ocean which, unlike the crashing of the waves upon the beach, are almost invisible in their expression. Being more powerful in our lives begins with realizing that we have the capacity for power. Many people inhibit their own power through the belief that they are powerless and have little or no command over their emotional well-being or life circumstances. Others defeat their power by falling into the trap of ego gratification and arrogance. It was Karlfried Graf Dürckheim who said, "Power does not corrupt men. It is men who rise to positions of authority, who corrupt power."

Faith: Trust, Surrender & Unity

Trust, from the Old Norse root "traust," means "to rely on one's self." The original definition referred more to trusting oneself than to trusting others. In fact, the only way to determine whether another is trustworthy is to have enough self-trust to assess them accurately. Gaining more self-trust is a function of taking risks, learning from our experiences and continuing to stay open while we engage in the process. Although it's difficult to open up after a painful betrayal or violation, it is exactly the time we need to open. Staying closed not only keeps us "safe," it also stifles our ability to know the true power of faith.

There are many perspectives about trust, all of which have their assets and liabilities. One perspective is that we should protect ourselves from violation for fear of getting hurt. If we can be hurt, we can be wounded, and if wounded, disabled, and if disabled, we could die. This perspective helps us gauge how, when and where we should be open to trusting someone. The downside is that it inhibits our participation in life and reinforces our weaknesses. The perspective of needing protection also assumes we are not resilient enough to recover from a trust violation.

Another perspective on trust is actively trusting life through engaging in risks and growing from the mistakes we make along the way. Although we might get hurt, hurt often leads to growth, growth leads to strength, and strength leads to realizing how indestructible we really are. The downside is that we may take some risks that lead us into painful or damaging experiences. If we desire to gain more faith, however, regardless of our perspective on trust, we must place ourselves in situations that stretch us and open us to the possibilities.

Surrender is the act of voluntarily giving up claim or control over one's life to a higher power. Many people understand surrender to be a "white flag" phenomena indicating defeat or desperation. In some context, I'm sure the meaning is valid, but within the domain of faith it is far from accurate. Defeat and desperation involve succumbing or giving in to external pressure or authority. Surrender, on the other hand, is an internal act, involving the freedom of choice. Surrendering is a choice, not a necessity. That's not to say that necessity might not play a part in surrender, but the final act is initiated by choice, else it becomes subservience.

Surrender needn't be hierarchical. In other words, when surrendering ourselves, it can be from a spirit of partnership and equality rather than enslavement. Surrendering to feedback is a good example of this. Just because I ask for, respect, or accept your perceptions doesn't mean I have to obey you. This distinction is extremely valuable, especially in personal relationships, as it ensures individual sovereignty while maintaining an open channel for contribution between partners. The antithesis of surrender is idolization. When we idolize someone, in essence we are saying, "You are greater than I am, therefore I will worship and adore you." True surrender exists outside such frivolities. It flourishes within the realm of our vastness, our inherent greatness and the grace bestowed upon us by divine intervention.

Unity is the state of being one, or united as in a single organism. It embodies the quality of being one in spirit, sentiment and purpose. Because unity implies a symbiotic relationship with the universal, it includes sharing in the movement of cosmic order and disorder, the process of creation and destruction, and everything in between. In essence, unity extends to the ends of the universe and beyond the scope of time and space. In the experience of unity, there is no "I," "you," or even "us," as the bounds of identity are dispersed by the eternal hands of our maker. In unity "we" are individual expressions of one entity, one people, one race. Practicing the behavior of unity requires contemplating and staying aware of this interconnectedness, especially when we want to deny it.

Service: Contribution, Patience & Love

Contribution is the act of giving or providing jointly with others. When we contribute to someone, we are sharing in the process of making something happen with them. The difference between contributing and simply doing something for someone is that contribution is a "with" act rather than a "for" act. In other words, it is a collaborative deed rather than a directive one. Also, contribution carries no obligation. If there is any sense of feeling obliged, it is probably not a contributory act but a conciliatory one. This is important in terms of developing behaviors consistent with being of service. If we allow ourselves to function from obligation for too long, resentment, apathy and resistance begin to manifest. The best way to break obligatory behavior, if it's present, is to find a venue for contribution where your giving is not expected, but appreciated—but don't feel obligated to take this advice or it won't work.

Patience is the ability to wait without complaining or losing self-control. In today's fast-paced society, it is extremely difficult to be patient; however, without it, our stress level escalates, our sense of inner peace is shattered and our most valuable relationships often suffer. Patience isn't just a virtue, it's also a discipline. Patience requires a commitment to refusing to be provoked or angered through insult, perceived incompetence or lack of consideration. Developing steadfastness, diligence and perseverance is a worthy challenge. Those who possess these qualities command respect and are held in high regard. Patience doesn't mean we never express our frustration or the struggles we experience in our interactions with others, but it does mean having enough self-awareness to monitor such feelings and at least give warning that turbulence is about to occur. Such consideration fosters responsibility and respect. It also gives us a moment to exercise the discipline of not abusing the person with whom we are trying to be patient.

Love, from the Old English word, "lufu," means "to be fond of and to have a deep and tender feeling of affection for." There are as many definitions of love as there are people in the world. Within the context of service, however, love is the ability to accept someone exactly as they are with no changes in their behaviors, style, beliefs or attitudes. To love another is to recognize that he or she is a unique individual, and that there is a bond or connection that ties us to him or her, either through association or reflection. In other words, if the person is unlike us, we associate with characteristics we don't have, traits that can give us another perspective, experience or realization about life. Rather than judge them negatively, by loving them we are able to see that, although we may not share the same set of behaviors and may not even agree with them, we accept them as aspects of a common humanity. If they are similar to us, then they are a reflection of familiarity and give us another perspective on ourselves. Either way, different or similar to us, other people in our lives represent an opportunity to extend compassion and understanding.

This last of the Seven Dimensions of Knowing, *Service*, is the perfect topic on which to end this book. I hope my stories and insights have served you. Although I don't know you personally, if you are both humbled and inspired by the sacredness of the world, then in a way, I *do* know you. It tells me there is a childlike and mature greatness about you, a greatness that has been forged by your willingness to step into the burn zone of your own life. Viewed from the perspective of the *Master's Light*, we are separate *and* we are the same. In looking beyond our individual "flames," we catch a fleeting glimpse of our eternal nature, a nature that expresses itself not in separation, but within a brilliant "flaming" that burns brightly within the soul of all humanity.

Val Jon relaxing near the Hitching Post of the Sun the morning after his climb.

AFTERWORD

Lodge thine heart
betwixt the virtue of the Gods
and the daring of desire
for such sweet suffering
shall surely enchant your soul

During the final stages of writing *Inca Fire! Light of the Masters*, I began to notice some additional shifts in my perception, and I thought it would be useful to include them. From the time I learned about the Seven Dimensions of Knowing, high atop the summit of Wayna Picchu, to this moment as I type these words, I have been experiencing marked increases in awareness and capability in both my personal and professional life. I have noticed a substantial deepening of my relationships in terms of the quality of conversation, trust levels and appreciation for differences. With my work, I experience renewed energy, enthusiasm and greater endurance. Additionally, I find myself daily gaining new and meaningful spiritual insights that bring me joy and fulfillment.

The most impressive result however, is that I have recently experienced a powerful integration of the Seven Dimensions of Knowing. The shift is away from needing to remember each dimension or the behaviors associated with them, to simply noticing when one or more of them is absent. Prior to this shift, I knew I would need to stay aware of them in order to apply them in my life. Subsequently, I worked hard to practice each of the seven dimensions and actively discussed them with my friends. Initially, I decided the way to integrate them into my daily life was to designate one dimension for each day of the week. The progression I used was:

Monday	Humility: Openness, Vulnerability & Compassion
Tuesday	Eternality: Resilience, Endurance & Indestructability
Wednesday	Truth: Authenticity, Groundedness & Objectivity
Thursday	Passion: Enthusiasm, Inspiration & Aspiration
Friday	Sovereignty: Respect, Autonomy & Power
Saturday	Faith: Trust, Surrender & Unity
Sunday	Service: Contribution, Patience & Love

After I assigned them, I wrote the sequence on a notepad and stuck it on my refrigerator door so I would notice it each morning. I then made a point to emulate the three behaviors for that day in my interactions. Although a bit linear, this "self-coaching" scheme kept me aware of the seven dimensions and helped me apply them to my daily circumstances. The scheme worked so well that within about three weeks, I naturally knew "what day" it was. As the weeks passed, I felt a deepening of my natural awareness until, in almost any situation or conversation, I knew which dimensions and behaviors were present and which were absent. This shift away from trying to stay aware of them, to simply noticing when they were absent, reminded me of learning how to snow ski. As a beginner, it was all about remembering the key moves and watching every move I made to avoid falling. After some time on the slopes, my perception shifted, and I didn't need to remember anything because I was too busy skiing.

I was also intrigued when I experienced additional memories as a result of being aware of the Seven Dimensions of Knowing. These reflections were remarkable because, rather than viewing them through only one dimension as I did on the summit of Wayna Picchu, I began witnessing them through multiple dimensions, sometimes all seven simultaneously. It was like looking into my life with a kaleidoscope of seven "lenses." Each lens colored the images I saw in a different way, providing me with a rainbow of insights. For example, as I read my story about Sam Lono, the Hawaiian Kahuna, I recalled an incident in which I lost a substantial amount of money due to an unscrupulous business partner. The incident stood out for me because of the resentment and anger I still harbored. A fascinating insight was that, at first, without looking through any of the dimensions, I perceived myself in the event as an innocent victim betrayed by an artful swindler. Looking through the lenses of *Truth* and *Sovereignty*, however, I didn't see myself as a total victim. I realized I had played a part in the betrayal because I had not stood up for myself earlier in the relationship. I saw that by not being true to myself and by stepping over a series of inequities and controlling maneuvers, I had cast my own fate.

Taking responsibility for my part in the betrayal empowered me in two ways: I was able to release my resentment; and I learned that I must stay true to myself under all circumstances. Looking once again at the incident, this time through the lenses of *Humility, Eternality and Passion*, even though it is very painful to be betrayed, I realize that I must remain open and not close myself to new partnerships. Closing because of the possibility of hurt would be more damaging than forging a new business relationship and risking another violation. Looking through the lenses of *Faith* and *Service*, I realize that I will always get stronger even during the worst situations and that the best way to serve others and myself is to be willing to engage fully in life. I also see that I possess the strength, endurance and enthusiasm needed to lay a positive business foundation when the opportunity arises.

Because opening to the wisdom held within the *Light of the Masters* is an ever-evolving process, I suspect there will be many more insights to follow. As a way to stay in touch and share those future insights, I invite you to visit my web site at www.incafire.com. In addition to newly posted information about the Seven Dimensions of Knowing, the site contains photographs, event and book-signing schedules, a poster and videotape section, a Peruvian gift catalog, Inca tour information, a reader's bulletin board and live author/reader forums. Please feel free to log on any time, explore the site and share with other like-minded seekers the insights you gain as you step into the burn zone of your own life. Again, it has been a privilege to serve you. May you always feel blessed by everything that comes to you in your life.

ORDERING

Order *Inca Fire! Light of the Masters* directly from the author for $22.95 per copy. Add $3.00 for shipping & handling for the first copy and $1.50 for each additional copy. Quantity discounts available for distributors and wholesalers. Make checks payable to:

Keystone Group
10556 Combie Road #6478
Auburn, CA 95602

To order by credit card call toll free 1-877-INCAFIRE (allow 2 weeks for delivery). Posters, videotapes, events, photos and support services are available on our web site: **www.incafire.com**

Join the *Inca Fire! On–Line Forum* and receive a discount on our color poster. (See next page for sample.)

Four-color, varnished, high-gloss posters available. Large: 24 inches by 36 inches; Small: 19 inches by 28 inches. To order, visit our website or call us toll free at 1-877-INCAFIRE.

REFERENCES

Art of the Andes from Chavin to Inca, Rebecca Stone Miller.
(Thames and Hudson, 1995) ISBN: 0-500-20286-9.

Empire of the Inca, Burr Cartwright Brundage.
(University of Oklahoma Press, 1985) ISBN: 0-8061-1924-1.

Machu Picchu Historical Sanctuary, Peter Frost and Jim Bartle.
(Nuevas Imagenes S. A., 1995) ISBN: 99-2-9015-00-5.

Peru Travel Survival Kit, Rob Rachowiecki.
(Lonely Planet, 1996) ISBN: 0-86442-3322.

The Sacred Valley of the Incas Myths and Symbols, Fernando E.
Elorrieta Salazar and Edgar Elorrieta Salazar.
(Sociedad Pacaritanpu Hatha, 1996)